from Cinders *to* Butterflies

A Spiritual Journey to Healing

Richard B. Fratianne, M.D.

PORTLAND • OREGON

ISBN 1-59299-018-5

Franklin Street Books
6750 SW Franklin
Portland, OR 97223
www.franklinstreetbooks.com

Printed in the U.S.A.

Dedication

*This book is dedicated to my wonderful wife Mary,
my bride of forty-seven years. Her constant and
unwavering devotion and support have been pillars
of strength for me throughout our life together.
Whatever happiness I may have enjoyed in my life is
rooted in her love for me. Whatever my accomplishments
may have been, I owe to my faithful and loving wife Mary.*

*This book is also dedicated to my patients who,
by their triumph over adversity and suffering,
have taught me the reality of my faith in God and
the power He gives us to be transcendent.*

Acknowledgements

I wish to pay special tribute to Cathie Noga for all she has contributed in making this book a reality. Her expertise and tireless efforts on my behalf are gratefully appreciated.

TABLE OF CONTENTS

No one can look upon a person who has survived a serious burn injury and not feel at least a twinge of fear or discomfort and maybe even a sense of loathing at the sight of the twisted distortion of the scars they see. Despite the marvels of modern plastic surgery, the scars are forever! The unfortunate people who suffer serious burns, therefore, have an incurable disease. My spiritual journey has led me to the realization that my patients needed more than just my skills as a surgeon, which is to care for them and close their wounds with skin grafts. Burns occur from the "outside in;" burned patients needed to be healed, and that process occurs from the "inside out." Helping to heal patients who have suffered such devastating injuries is not a "one-man job." This book describes a very special group of dedicated medical professionals who responded to the invitation to join together as a spirit-filled team of expert caregivers, dedicated to the vision that burn patients *can* be healed even though their scars are incurable. In order to assemble such a team, I learned to center my professional life on an axis of values that witness to the command to "love God and love your neighbor as yourself," and lead by example. The results of our efforts can best be described as transforming the charred ravages of *burn injured victims,* ("ugly, lifeless cinders") into *burn survivors,* ("beautiful butterflies") who learned that their beauty comes from within; that, they can live fulfilling, meaningful and happy lives, filled with confidence, dignity, self-esteem and true inner beauty. An added dimension has been the realization that I, and the members of my burn team, have also been transformed in the process of helping others become healed of their suffering. We too have become butterflies!

It is a remarkable journey of Faith, Hope and above all, Love.

One of my fondest memories growing up as the second oldest in a family of five children, in the depression years following the events of 1929, is a conversation with my mother. We talked about my dreams and my dilemma; on the one hand I thought I should become a priest, and on the other I had this unquenchable desire to become a surgeon. I remember my mother telling me, time and time again, that I should do whatever I thought was best. She was skillful at building my self-confidence and was my inspiration to persevere in following my dreams for the future.

She made a remark then that has stayed with me throughout my life; that was, "You know, son, you could be both." I was puzzled by her remark and did not quite understand how that could be possible. In later years I came to understand that what she meant was that it was not necessary to separate our secular life from our spiritual life; but rather, to live our secular life as a manifestation of our spirituality. I define spirituality as our relationship with God; and religion as a relationship with a "church." Religious participation is designed to foster our relationship with God. "Religion" is therefore a means to the end, not the end itself. The true end is a loving, personal and intimate relationship with God in this, our human life on earth. Permit me to interject at this time. I use the term God based upon my religious orientation. Others can substitute Yahweh, Allah, The Creator, My Higher Power or whatever is most comfortable for them in referring to the Power Greater than Themselves. In reality, there is only one God for us all. I do not believe it makes any difference what we call that Power. It is the recognition of that Supreme Being which is most important.

That understanding, perhaps most of all, has led me to take up the challenge to put into words, the personal, professional and spiritual growth that has occurred in my life and made it possible for me to live out my mother's words in a way I never dreamed possible.

The Catholicism I learned in the days before the second Vatican Council could be characterized as "pay, pray and obey." The teachings of the Church were quite rigid and straightforward. I tried to do all the things I was instructed to do, including attending Mass every Sunday, making my Easter Duty and the nine First Fridays; and as I grew to adulthood, regular contributions in the Sunday basket. Despite doing all the "right" things, I always had the nagging feeling there was something more to faith than I was experiencing. I kept searching, but the answers kept eluding me. As the years went by, life became more complicated and began moving at a faster and faster pace. I had less and less time to search for the meaning of faith in my life.

At the same time my professional career was taking shape. I graduated from college and entered medical school in 1954. Two years later I met Mary, a strong and courageous woman who continues to give me strength through her boundless love. Together we overcame the struggles of seven years of post-graduate training, living in near poverty among the poor in the Metropolitan Housing

Projects of Cleveland and beginning our family of five beautiful children.

Life kept moving at an ever increasing pace and with all of the events crowding into my consciousness, I was becoming more and more dissatisfied with what I understood about my Church and what it had been able to give to me to help guide me through these difficult times. I was slowly and inexorably reaching a crisis point in my faith life when I had an encounter with the living Jesus that changed my life forever.

The spiritual life I now lead can be characterized as deeply gratifying yet simple and straightforward. Let me say at the beginning, I do not believe in magic; but I believe that miracles do happen. They are unexpected events arranged by God for those who have "eyes to see and ears to hear." All things in the universe work through the incredibly marvelous natural law God has created, along with the Presence of His Spirit alive within each of us. My spiritual journey can best be summarized in the words of St. John, "Those who abide in love abide in God and God in them." I am not a Scripture scholar, but God has taught me much through the events of my life and through the people He has given me to share my life; my family, my friends and perhaps most of all, my patients. He has led me to an ever-deepening spiritual growth through the simple application of His great commandment, to love God and to love your neighbor as yourself. It has been a richly rewarding and joy-filled journey that has sustained me in times of triumph and tragedy.

Roots and Wings

"...His mother kept all these sayings in her heart." Luke 3: 51

This is the first Mother's Day I have ever experienced when my mother was not with me. It is exactly one month since the angels came to escort her into Paradise. As I write this, my mind is flooded with memories, each of which captures a small facet of this simple lady. She had minimal formal education but a depth of spirituality that gave her enormous strength to face life's challenges. She had such great wisdom that she was able to serve as the rock, the foundation upon which I have built my entire personal and professional life—the foundation that has allowed me to become the person I am.

The greatest gift she possessed was her ability

and willingness to love others, just as they were. She had the courage to accept others with all their faults and to love unconditionally anyone who would accept her love. Mom could turn the other cheek and forgive those who in any way hurt her, devalued her or disrespected her. As the first child of Italian immigrants born in America, she was frequently the subject of prejudice and rude treatment because of her dress and demeanor. Undaunted, she was always willing to help others "carry their burdens" and to give hope to those who had none. Her life was founded on a faith that was simple in concept but profound in application.

I remember back when I was 11 or 12 years old. Mom knew that I had always dreamed of being a surgeon. There was, however, always this nagging feeling or doubt that perhaps I should seek the priesthood instead. I remember many comforting conversations when Mom and I discussed our choice and finally she said to me, "You must be a surgeon, but you can also be a priest." At the time, of course, I could not make sense out of that but I had Mom's support and that affirmed my dream even though I really did not understand what she meant about being a priest and a doctor until much later in my life. I remember how she seemed to have a sixth sense that knew some way or other what I was thinking and how I was feeling. She always seemed to know what I needed—sometimes a boot in the behind, sometimes a loving arm around me, sometimes a pull on my ear to give me a sense of direction, sometimes just making me something special to eat.

I became aware, at a young age, that no matter how tired or distressed she was about any situation or problem she faced, she not only looked after my needs but she did it with a grace that made her joyful. I do not remember her ever complaining, feeling sorry for herself, or blaming others for whatever the situation she faced. In spite of all the hardships she faced rearing five children in the depths of the Depression, she had a knack of making me feel like I was the most important person in her life. In later years, I came to understand that many, many people felt the same way. I often heard my Dad agree. My brother Douglas, who holds a doctorate in Botany, my three sisters, Betty a physician, Anita a pastoral care counselor and Mary Joy a Sister in the Humility of Mary Order, and just about anyone with whom her life interacted all came away from their experiences with her with that feeling as well. When asked one day at an awards banquet, "How did you ever raise such a wonderful family?" she responded, "I just loved them to death." I reminded her that in reality she had loved us to *life*. She was good at that.

I remember the tremendous encouragement she gave me when I decided that Mary was the person with whom I wished to spend my life. I was under considerable pressure from my parents because Mary was not of Italian background, not a Catholic and her parents' values were difficult for them to comprehend. Mary's folks did not approve of me and this caused us considerable stress. Mom was the only one who asked me, "Do you really love her?" and "Do you think she really loves you?" I told her, "Yes" to both questions and her response was, "Well then do it and do not worry about what anyone says."

Mom was there to support Mary and me, with her joyful hope and promise of the future, when Mary's parents banished her from their home and refused to attend our wedding. They did not understand why she chose a second generation Italian Catholic to marry. Mary's mother's family went back to the Mayflower and they were of the Episcopalian faith. Her father was Scottish and served as a pilot in the Royal Air Force during the First World War. I thank God for the support Mom gave me at that critical time in my life. I can not begin to think what my life would have become were it not for Mary, our children, the wonderful families they nurture and the beautiful grandchildren they have given us. The strength and support Mary has given me through the difficult times of our family life and my professional life has been solid, unwavering and reassuring.

Soon after we were married, Mary and I moved into the Metropolitan Housing Projects on the near west side of Cleveland. We lived there during my last two years in medical school and all through my post-graduate residency training. It is a tribute to the love that Mary has for me as well as for her parents, that even though she had been hurt deeply by their unwillingness to accept our marriage, Mary continued to love and respect them. After our second child was born, she fostered reconciliation with her parents so that they were able to enjoy the fullness of our relationship and the gifts of five beautiful grandchildren. It was one of my earliest experiences of the truth of the saying, "love conquers all."

The beautiful outcome of what could have been a sad story was truly a measure of the incredible depth of love that Mom was able to show all of us. I truly believe that Mary's ability to love so unselfishly was inspired, in part, by the example that my mother had given to her by the depth of Mom's love for the two of us. Mom was our teacher and our guide through many difficult times in our early life together and the lessons we learned helped us immeasurably in our later years.

It was towards the end of my residency when I was beginning my academic career that Mom gave me a hand written prayer that I have kept before me on my desk for the last 40 years. It says, *"God will not look you over for medals, degrees or diplomas but for scars suffered for the sake of others."* With that prayer she closed the circle of what she meant when she told me I could be both priest and physician. She understood that a priest is a person who helps people find a relationship with God, and that the way I practiced medicine could also accomplish that goal. As I moved through my career, it was her faith in me that I could be a "healer of patients who were suffering" that became the foundation upon which my career has been built. It remains today as a testament of Mom's life-giving love for me—the gift of faith and hope she above all passed on to me.

My life is blessed with many relationships with wonderful loving and inspiring people, but none more important than Mom. Her faith was simple, her willingness to sacrifice herself for others was boundless, her ability to touch others' lives was immense and her love was truly without end. Her life was a testament to unconditional, sacrificial love.

On the one hand, this is a very difficult day for me. Recalling these glorious memories, which flash across my mind, has confirmed my belief that love never dies. The inspiration my Mother has given me continues to live on in everything I do. Thank you for both the physical life and the "inner life" you have given me. "Happy Mother's Day, Mom."

Keys

"I will give you the keys to the kingdom." Matthew 16: 19

From my earliest memories, I always wanted to be around my Dad. Wherever he went I went. Although we did not always do things that I chose to do, I was always comfortable in his presence. Whether riding with him in the car on one of his business calls or caddying for him on the golf course, I enjoyed whatever it was we did together. Of my three sisters and my brother, I believe I had the closest attachment to him for reasons that I can not explain, but to this day, 27 years after his death, I still feel a tremendous affection for him.

As I look back and try to analyze what it was that created the special bond we had, two things stand out in my mind. First, he was the most honest person I have ever known. I knew I could always trust him and he gave me a solid sense of security. His word truly was his bond and an agreement with my father did not require a contract. This mentality characterized all of his relationships regardless of the party involved and whatever were the circumstances of the agreement. I think he trusted others, and his mind-set engendered trust in him. I was always impressed by that attitude and he would tell me over and over, "Do right and fear not." The second thing that I recall is that he always reminded me, "Be a leader." When I was young I really did not understand what that meant. However, as I grew, I came to realize that what he meant was not following the crowd and doing things that everybody wanted to do, if I thought it was wrong or if I did not want to do them. More importantly, I learned to use the values he had given me and only do things that I felt were right even if it was unpopular with my friends. He told me many times, "Have the courage of your convictions; you know what is right and wrong. A leader forges his own path and does not let other people dictate to him or influence his decisions."

What made his words echo true in my heart was the fact that he was an extremely disciplined individual. That he could discipline himself to do what needed to be done, I believe, was a component of his honesty. In almost every case, even though it may have been difficult or what was expected of him was unpleasant, he somehow found the strength to do what needed to be done. As I was growing into adulthood I came to understand more deeply what made him "tick." He was an outstanding example of a father and a mentor. As I reflect back to my younger days, I realize how fortunate I was to have had him for a dad. He gave me a sense of security and inner strength that helped me gain self-respect and formulate my vision of life as a father to my children and as a physician.

His attitudes of honesty, commitment and discipline characterized my life as I was going to school. He told me that a disciplined body will help to discipline the mind; so whenever I had an exam in high school or in college for that matter, I always dressed in a suit and tie, even though almost everyone around me was in jeans and sweatshirts. I felt more confident having his words echo in my mind and I clearly owe a great deal of my academic success in my life to the principles of living that my father passed on to me. He really touched every aspect of my life and I believe I am the recipient of a great gift from my Dad.

One of the great stories my Dad told me may help you to understand who he was and why he meant so much in my life. When Dad was 14 years old, he caddied at one of the local private country clubs. In 1919, the pay for a class B caddy (beginner) was 35 cents a round and a class A caddy (senior) was 50 cents a round. Dad told me that one day after he finished caddying, the gentleman gave him his pay and he took off on his borrowed bicycle to get himself home. He was very happy because the man had given him a dollar. On the way home, he looked at the bill and saw it was a ten dollar bill. He realized that this could not possibly be the correct payment because in those days men worked an entire week for less than ten dollars.

He peddled back to the country club and found the gentleman for whom he had caddied in the men's grille playing cards. He apologetically interrupted the man and said, "Sir, I caddied for you today," and the gentleman turned and said, "Oh yes, I remember and you did a very nice job." My

Dad retorted, "Sir, you gave me a ten dollar bill." The man looked startled and saw the bill in my father's hand and took it back and said, "Yes, son, I meant to give you a dollar." And then he said, "I have never met a more honest young man." Finally he said something that was later to change my father's life. He told him, "If you ever need a job, you come to see me," and he gave him one of his business cards. His name was William A. Howe. He owned a printing establishment that made die-cut images for advertising purposes. Ten years later in the depth of the Great Depression, my mother and dad and my older sister were struggling to make ends meet, as was most everyone in the country. My father went to ask Mr. Howe for a job. When he went in to see him he said, "Sir, you may remember I caddied for you at the Shaker Country Club one day and you gave me a ten-dollar bill." The man immediately remembered my dad and said, "Young man you have a job." I was born shortly thereafter, and so while the country was really suffering with the Great Depression, my father and mother were able to survive with a decent standard of living that helped me get started in life with many advantages. My father went on to a business career in newspaper advertising, building on his experiences in the printing business.

Dad also told me many times how he wished he had been able to have a college education. He told me a remarkable story. When he left school after completing eighth grade he knew he was not prepared to do anything except manual labor. For some reason, as a first generation American with parents who came from Italy with no education to speak of, he enrolled and completed a correspondence course from The LaSalle Extension University located in Chicago, Illinois. He received what we would now call a G.E.D. It always impressed me that he was so committed to education. He did something I thought was extraordinary. He was the only member of his family, which included two brothers and three sisters, to ever have any form of completed education. As my older sister Betty Jean and I, my younger brother Douglas and two younger sisters Anita and Mary Joy grew up, we always knew we would be going to college. Dad would have it no other way.

Dad also knew of my dream to be a physician and it was an unequivocal belief on his part that I would be able to accomplish my goal. It was not in any way a demand on his part. It was a lot of confidence building, with his assurances that I should believe in myself and know that I could do what was necessary to gain admission to the medical profession even though the opportunities for admission to medical schools in the 1950s were extremely restricted. Our family had limited means and I would have to work my way through college and medical school, but I came to believe I could do it.

At the rather early age of 67, my father developed a cancer of the esophagus, which, despite all of the technology of modern medicine, took his life in two years. My father's favorite of all holidays was Christmas. The most important day he wished all of his children could be with him was Christmas Eve. We had a traditional Christmas Eve dinner, as many folks do, and ours was an Italian experience going back many generations. I remember quite clearly Dad's last Christmas Eve. He was hospitalized at the time. We spent the afternoon together sharing memories and a few laughs. We both recognized that this would be his last Christmas and despite the sharing, he was very sad. This would be the first Christmas Eve he ever missed being with his family. The entire family was gathering at his home and he was not going to be there.

When the time came, I found it difficult to leave, seeing how sad he was, but he told me something that gave me great consolation. He said he was praying that all the people that he might have ever offended in his life would come to visit him before he died so he could apologize to them. My father was an outspoken person who said what he thought and oftentimes gave the impression that he was uncaring about the feelings of the person with whom he was speaking. I know it was not out of meanness, but many people interpreted his directness and some of his remarks that way. For him to say that he was praying for the opportunity to ask forgiveness told me quite clearly that he had reached a peaceful acceptance of his weaknesses, as he prepared for his impending death. It was an incredible display of strength and humility as he prepared for death. It was a powerful display of faith and hope that would serve me well when I thought I was facing my death from brain cancer.

I reminded him that his prayer was an act of love on his part and that it was a reflection of the love that he had given to me. He had taught me what parental love really is; deep, abiding, sacrificial and unconditional. I asked him to always remember that what he had taught me was what I was trying to pass on to my children, to the best of my ability. I told him I hoped that I could do as good a job with my children as he had done with me. *I also told him people may die, but loving relationships do not die. The love that was between us would live forever. Love never dies; it just gets passed on.*

The love of which I speak can not be explained or taught. *In order to be understood, it must be experienced.* Until you believe you are loved unconditionally, you can not truly understand what it means. How fortunate I am to have had a mother and father who so graciously helped me experience the love that continues to fill my life. Once we have experienced unconditional love, we can pass it on to others. By passing it on, each of us can become an instrument, an example to others, and thereby help them to understand the meaning of true love—God's Love. God loves each of us, unconditionally For me, the personification of that love is Jesus Christ. The Keys to the kingdom are revealed by His message to "love one another as I have loved you." As I left the hospital, I was in tears—tears of sadness and tears of joy, but mostly sadness, that Dad could not come home with me. Although he passed away 27 years ago, I remember him daily in my morning offering and recount the gifts he gave me that helped direct my life on the path that I have followed.

Approximately six months after he died, the cemetery planted a small tree next to his grave. On one of my frequent visits, on a beautiful clear and bright day in spring, while I was praying and wishing we could be together, a sudden gust of wind came up and I felt a "squeeze" on both of my shoulders. I was startled and turned around to see who had come up behind me. All I saw was this young sapling flashing back to its upright position. I realized that the wind had bent the tree towards me and the tender branches at the lower part of the tree had encircled my shoulders. I stood there totally overwhelmed in the knowledge that God had sent me one more hug from my Dad. As I recall that day at this wonder-filled moment, I can still feel his "arms" around me. It brings back the memory that one of the last times he saw me he looked deeply into my eyes and said, "I love you, son." Thanks for the "keys," Dad.

THREE

Freedom to Choose

"Man does not live by bread alone." Matthew 4: 4

As I was going through college and then medical school, I always thought I was destined to be a medical missionary and walk in the footsteps of my hero, Albert Schweitzer. That seemed the most reasonable way to fulfill the words of my mother, to be both priest and physician. Life as a young adult became quite rigorous. Working to pay tuition and trying to get grades in college that would make my application to medical school competitive left little time for introspection and planning except for the immediate future. After receiving my medical degree, I was plunged into a life that could best be described as hectic and exhausting. Post-graduate residency training in surgery required total concentration. There was so much to learn and also so much to do. For the first time, I was experiencing the impact of patients' lives depending on me! 'Survival' left little time for wife and family or friends. At the same time life was challenging, exciting and wonder-filled. I was starting to feel like a doctor! The idea that I was destined to be a medical missionary in order to fulfill the words of my mother to be both priest and physician became like a dream from the distant past. I was forced to keep focused on the physical and mental challenges I was facing during the years of my postgraduate training. I was "on call" and in the hospital 36 out of every 48 hours. Being a medical missionary was nice to think about but not really important to me during those demanding days of surgical residency. Most of the time, I was stressed to the point of near exhaustion.

In those days, the stipend for surgical residents was extremely meager and Mary and I struggled to make ends meet. We were raising our family, by then three children under the age of five, in near poverty, living among the poor in the Metropolitan Housing Projects of Cleveland on the near west side of town. Fortunately there were many families of fellow residents living in the projects, which helped make living there bearable for Mary and the children. Mary bore the entire responsibility for looking after the children, certainly not an easy task. To this day I ask myself how she possibly could have done what she did for so long, and did it so well!

What more could I have asked for? I had a beautiful wife who loved me, and wonderful children coming along. How tempting it was for me to start dreaming about the material wealth I would be able to command. My thoughts moved away from thinking about serving God and looking forward to a practice that would ensure that I could provide a comfortable living for my wife and family, and give us a measure of security we had never known. Perhaps I would achieve recognition in the community and even academically if every thing went well. What I did not realize was that I was rushing head long into a choice I was not prepared to make. It was easy for me to rationalize my feelings as I told myself that prudence demands a father look after his family in order to provide for a certain amount of security and well being, especially in times of illness or financial distress. Without that, life could seem to be overwhelming and the children would be deprived of a feeling of safety. I could not, however, clear my conscience of the nagging doubt about seeking for material wealth and comfort.

The choice, in reality, is to what extent we allow ourselves to be governed by self-seeking material wealth versus being willing to live our lives in a sharing and caring manner in which others are seen as fellow travelers down the difficult road of life. Human nature tends to make us look after ourselves first, whereas God is asking us to live our lives in community with reverence for each other. That conflict faces every person and is present throughout our life times. Unfortunately, it is not a one-time decision, but requires a response every day because circumstances change in our lives and feelings and frustrations ebb and flow constantly. It was reinforced to me many times that *the free choices we make determine the life we lead.*

Fortunately, for Mary and me, there came a time when our faith was able to jog my mind into thinking, more clearly, about the choices I was being forced to make. My thoughts went back to Scripture as I began to realize that Jesus Himself went through these same decisions when He began His public life. While we can not comprehend what is the totality of the Divinity of Christ, we know He is a Divine Person. We also know He was truly human and subject to all that is part of our own humanity. I realized that if I confined my thoughts only to His humanity, it would be possible to understand His response *as a man* to His temptation in the desert by the devil. That way I would be able to use Him as an example of how I should lead my life in response to the challenges I was facing.

Let us place our mind's eye back to the events following His baptism in the Jordan River. As the Man emerged from the water, He must have been aware that God was calling Him to do something very special with His life. He surely came to realize He was being asked to proclaim, by the example of His life, what He believed about God, the Father. It is His *humanity* that makes all of the suffering He endured throughout His lifetime a testament of His *faith*. We do not often think about Jesus having sore feet, or a headache or having to go to the 'bath room.' But He was human in all things, just like us! Without being truly human, His passion would not be true suffering, as we know it as human beings.

His humanity must have filled Him with all the doubts and worries we all face. The man, Jesus, did not know how everything would 'work out' in the end any more than we do, but our faith, like His, reassures us that God has a plan for each of us.

Emerging from the water, there must have been a 'tug of war' going on inside Him. The Man must have wondered, "Am I really the One Who is supposed to go out and proclaim this magnificent ideal of life lived in union with God? Is this really what I'm supposed to do with My life?" He had studied Scripture. His mother, Mary, and Joseph taught Him well and He knew all the prophets who had spoken on behalf of God. He knew the price they had paid to be God's voice. His strength came from His intimate, loving relationship with His Father and this gave Him the courage to make the choice to follow His Father's plan. Pain, suffering and death would surely await Him if He chose to go down the path outlined in Scripture for the Son of Man to follow. His human feelings must have caused Him to pause. He decided go into the desert to contemplate.

His mind must have been filled with questions. From a human perspective, "What is God calling me to do? Must I answer the call?" Jeremiah protested he was too young and Moses protested because he stuttered—but they answered the call of God. They, too, must have faced these same questions, as did all the prophets who felt called by God to proclaim Him in the world.

Scripture portrays Jesus as being visited by the devil. I believe the devil is the awareness within us that we mortals instinctively seek for ourselves security, wealth, power and recognition by others. The devil personifies greed, self-centeredness, pride and arrogance. When carried to the extreme, giving into the temptations of the devil means thinking only of self-gratification, that is being willing to use others for our personal gain regardless of the costs to others and perhaps, even to ourselves! The devil is portrayed as asking Jesus, in His *humanity*, to make three choices. First, he says, "Let me help you seek after material things in order to satisfy your human instincts." Second, "Let me make you become more concerned for yourself than for others, so you will gain fame, fortune and glory through the admiration of others." And third, "Let me show you how to form God in *your* image so that you will feel righteous in doing what you choose to do, even if it is self-centered. That way you will not feel guilty at 'disobeying God's command.'"

We know how Jesus responded to His tempta-tion; but every one of us goes through this same tug-of-war process, beginning at some point in our life when we become mature enough to know we have to make choices and develop a value system by which to live our lives. What Jesus faced in that encounter with the devil is exactly what each of us faces all through our lives. If we reflect on our younger days, each of us who professes to be a Christian will recognize that there was such a point in our lives. That could be called our 'desert' expe-rience—when we were tempted by worldly desires and were forced to choose either a life of material wealth that is self-centered, or a life which is devoted to living the Christian ideal. Anyone who professes to follow Jesus faces this choice everyday. What we need most of all is a personal, intimate and loving relationship with the Father.

I became aware that I was being asked these same questions. Conflicting feelings developed in my conscience because I was afraid I was heading down the wrong path! "How do *I* make these choices? What is it that God is asking *me* to do with my life? Should I live for myself or should I live for others?" There was no escape for me. I had reached that point of my life when I had to choose, and I was afraid! I was terrified! "How do I balance my spiritual life with my secular life? Am I being honest with myself or am I deceiving myself?" I felt uneasy. What comforted me then, and what continues to comfort me now, is the way Jesus responded to His encounter with the devil.

Each day Jesus had to make these same choices we have to make. Had He not *freely* chosen to follow the path of living the prophetic life, there would have been no New Testament for us, no Good News! *His free choices determined the life He lived!* Every time He felt human weakness, as though He was not living up to His calling, His commitment, He went off by Himself, on "retreat," to gain spiritual strength through prayer. He had to re-examine Himself, to look inside Himself to ask, "Father give Me the strength I need to continue living My ideal of life?" We know He found that strength through regular prayer and meditation, and that is exactly what I needed to do, but did not realize what that meant at that time in my life. I was lost in a sea of confusion and apprehension as I came to the crossroads of my life. *My free choice would determine the life I, and my family, would lead.*

With Mary's undying love and support for me, we did find strength through prayer, and found our way through the shifting sands of our human existence. I have come to believe that for any of us who profess that we are living a Christian life, it must be a daily process of examination of self, and a recommitment to our principles and value system we profess. Then we must go out and do our best to live out those principles. At the end of each day I find it helpful to reflect on how well I have been true to myself. Many times, I feel the pangs of remorse that I have not done better, especially when I have turned away from others who were in need or who have asked for my help. I think we all need to ask for the strength to try to do better the next day, asking God to help us freely choose to do what He is asking us?

The realization that Jesus, the Man, went through the same gut-wrenching choices I had to endure gave me great consolation and strength. I began to believe I could make difficult choices with the help of God, through the example of the life of

Jesus. Even though I was not exactly sure what it was I should do, I knew that God understood, first-hand, what I was going through. He had gone through the same difficulties Himself. Mary and I knew we had a long way to go in order to get through residency training and that many difficulties lay before us, but we felt we were now heading in the right direction together. What a profound consolation amidst the hectic pace of our lives!

The Vision

"What you do for the least of My people, you do for Me."
Matthew 25: 40

Mary showed the depth of her unconditional love for me in many ways, but one
of the most profound demonstrations
happened as I was completing my internship. I was
offered a job to work as a family doctor in my sister Betty's Family Practice office at a guaranteed
annual salary of $30,000. In 1959, that was a great
deal of money. The salary for a surgical resident in
training was $1,500 per year. The family was living
in near poverty with borrowed furniture and hand-
me-down clothes. We had large loans taken in
order to complete medical school. Fortunately, we
did not have to repay them until I finished my
training. There was nothing extra for recreation
and we could not even afford a movie let alone a

vacation. Disaster loomed if our old car broke down. It was life on the edge of survival. Four of our children were born into these conditions.

I thought I should take the offer in order to give Mary and the children a better life. It meant giving up my dream of being a surgeon, but under the circumstances, this choice seemed clear to me. I felt I had to accept it. Mary made a courageous decision. In essence she said, "We can survive whatever we must go through for as long as we need to! You are going to be a surgeon!" Mary's response overwhelmed me. How totally unselfish and loving was her decision to forego security and material benefits. It was like an arrow piercing my heart that rekindled in me those old feelings of my mission to be both priest and physician. How could I not respond in the face of Mary's loving sacrifice? Of course, what she was consigning herself to, was an additional five years of near poverty. I was assigned to be on duty, in the hospital 36 out of every 48 hours. Because of our lack of funds, we had no choice but to take advantage of the fact that the hospital provided my meals free and we could buy extra dinners for forty cents, in the cafeteria. It was the only way we could afford nutritious meals for the children! That meant Mary had the responsibility of transporting the children back and forth from the hospital each night, taking them home, by herself, when I had to stay at the hospital ... summer, winter, rain, snow, stressed, exhausted ... all to keep me going in my surgical training.

She had to bear in essence all the major responsibility for their care and nurturing. Mary was an only child and therefore had no prior knowledge about raising children. She had never bathed an infant until she gave our first born her first bath! She learned all these responsibilities "on the run." When I did come home I would be so exhausted I could not help her with the children. I never bathed them nor even changed a diaper that I can remember. I do not know how Mary was able to be up at night with feedings and then put in the kind of day little children demand. Imagine bundling children up in the dead of winter and carting them to the hospital, then being forced to keep them amused until I was able to join them for supper ... sometimes waiting up to an hour until I could get away from my duties! Yet with all the sacrifices Mary made, day after day and year after year, she did it with amazing grace. She bore what must have been overwhelming stress without ever making me feel guilty! Mary was driven by sheer determination that I would fulfill my dream of being a surgeon. She was as close to being a perfect wife and mother as anyone (I) could imagine.

Then I would be off to the hospital at 5:30 in the morning without waking Mary or the children, leaving total responsibility to her with a prayer of thanksgiving for her tremendous love and dedication to her family. What a fantastic demonstration of deep and abiding love she expressed by being willing to continue such a hectic and demanding life on my behalf. She helped me experience true unconditional love. I broke my sister's heart when I refused her offer, but clearly Mary and I were on a different path.

One day in my fourth year of residency Mary and I were talking about what we would be doing in the future, and what kind of practice I would try to develop. Our thoughts returned to the idea of following our original plan to be medical missionaries. We knew that would be a hard life with young children, but we felt we were destined to follow that course. Mary was committed to continue her life of total dedication to our vision. We began exploring options among various groups who sponsored medical missions. It seemed to me that Southeast Asia was the likely destination we would pursue. Dr. Tom Dooley was a wonderful young man, a graduate of Notre Dame University and a medical missionary who practiced in what would later be called Cambodia. As a young man, he developed a malignant melanoma that rapidly took his life. Perhaps Mary and I were destined to take up his efforts? We had many discussions about what to do. One day Mary made the comment, "I am ready to go and do whatever you feel is right, but I am not sure why we have to travel 12,000 miles to take care of poor people; they are all around us."

Her words struck me in a very powerful way. We were living among the poor of Cleveland who needed medical care and all the help they could find! Soon after that, with much prayer and meditation, we decided that what we were being called to do was to stay in Cleveland and provide medical care to the poor. The county hospital served as the safety net hospital for the poor in Cleveland, and therefore it seemed to be a good choice. Our decision felt comfortable because I was quite certain the hospital would remain committed to the care of the poor and the training I was receiving taught me a valuable sense of service and respect for the under-privileged and elderly. It was the most complete way we could live the vision that Mom had given me so many years before. We were ready to accept the fact that this meant we would have a relatively low income. There would be little prospect of fancy homes and big cars. Even with all these 'negatives,' the future looked promising and bright because we felt at peace with our decision.

We have never wavered from that commitment despite numerous opportunities to go elsewhere. Many of the offers we subsequently received over the years would have brought us wealth and acade-mic recognition but we have stayed the course and remained true to our commitment. There were many sacrifices that were required, especially raising and educating five children on a limited income. Looking back neither Mary, the children nor I have ever regretted the choices we made. We have, together, accomplished our goal of being "medical missionaries" to the poor of Cleveland.

Living out that commitment has helped both of us realize that we have been privileged to experience the special grace and power that God gives to those who serve the poor. For many of the poor, vulnerable, helpless and marginalized members of society, the depth of their faith can be witnessed in their response to illness, physical deprivations and prejudice. The poor have a strength of inner character which, I believe is "fine tuned" by the circumstances of their lives. The hardships they endure and over which they triumph are a testament to their ability to survive circumstances that would overwhelm most of us who live comfortable lives. Imagine having to stay awake at night, sleeping in shifts, in order to keep rats from biting your children while they sleep. I have seen it! Or having the gas disconnected and being in the dead of winter without heat and having to boil water on a hot plate to keep from freezing. I have seen that too! I have also seen children burned when the boiling water was spilled on them as they played. For many, roaches are common companions in their homes. Most do not choose to live that way but circumstances over which they have little or no control dictate that life for them. They are eager to share their "tragedies and triumphs" with anyone who cares to listen. What they need, most of all, is that somebody cares about them for who they are, in all their 'poverty' of spirit. We have received a great deal from our work with these patients. We came to understand His words, "that which you do for the least of My brothers and sisters you do for Me." The rewards are not measured in what they pay, but rather in what they share with those who treat them with respect. Mary and I have always felt 'richly compensated.'

As I look back, I see the unmistakable hand of the Spirit guiding us in our decisions and leading us on the life path we have chosen to follow. Despite times of doubts, we have found peace and joy in our choices. Sometimes the most difficult challenges result in the greatest triumph. The challenge is to persevere along the chosen path of our 'vision,' even when we are not sure we can or even if we should try. There is a Japanese proverb that states, "Vision without Action is merely a Daydream. Action without Vision is a Nightmare!" Little did we realize where our vision would take us as we put it into action!

FIVE

The Encounter

"You did not choose me; I chose you." John 15: 16

As I completed my training and began practicing my profession, life became very fulfilling and we were able to move out of the housing projects at long last. I had developed a referral practice for treating breast cancer and other complex cancer patients. However, three years after completing my residency training I was asked to alter my practice and become the director of the Burn Unit that was being established at the county hospital. My initial response was negative. I was committed to helping cancer patients overcome their disease and I was serving the needs of the poor and the elderly already. I felt I was serving God living my mission as priest and physician. Besides, I did not want to take care of burned people. They were so ugly and they had a terrible odor about them. In fact, in those days when burn care was not very sophisticated, when you entered a ward with a burned patient in the area, you immediately knew it. No amount of deodorant or air freshener could eliminate that odor. That was not for me! Besides, I already was treating the poor and those unable to pay for their care, and I had a challenging practice that was very fulfilling, both professionally and personally. I was struggling to provide security for my wife and children, struggling to make difficult decisions concerning the economic impact of practicing in the county hospital and now I was being asked to make a difficult decision in what was to be the primary thrust of my surgical career. I had to give up a promising practice that was quite fulfilling and take on the 'burden' of treating burn victims. That seemed to be just plain 'too much.' As a matter of fact, it might be said that I took the job "with my heels dug in."

The inner conflict of deciding what to do regarding my professional path was made even more difficult because of the frustration I encountered with my faith experience at Mass each Sunday. I recognized a growing dissatisfaction with what I was not receiving from attending church services. My life was becoming more and more hectic and I was not receiving the guidance I desperately needed to keep my life in order. The homilies I heard were not relating the gospel to me in a meaningful way. It was just at the time of the Second Vatican Council, and the documents from that encounter taught a new way for the laity to live our faith experiences. However, I felt that the Spirit of the Council was not being presented at Sunday Mass. I knew there had to be more that I could get from my religious beliefs but I, like many Catholics, did not know where to find it. The turmoil of choosing a new professional path, yet feeling my religion was not helping me decide what the right choice was, made me feel angry and betrayed.

Somehow, by the grace of God, Mary and I made the choice to begin the Burn Unit. Little did we realize that when we accepted the challenge to begin the Burn Unit, it would set in motion a life so different from what we had ever known; a life so filled with the grace of God that it would illuminate for me the spiritual journey that is the subject of this manuscript.

When I first began the Burn Center, the wonderful results I was to eventually experience were far from evident. When the public announcement was made that the Center was opening, each head nurse of the four adult surgical wards in the hospital threatened to resign if burn patients were placed in their units. There was, in fact, no designated area for the "Burn Unit." It began in the Surgical Intensive Care Unit as a single bed, draped with a plastic covering over aluminum tubing that could be unzipped to allow the caregiver to enter this "closed environment."

I found myself with little help. No house staff was assigned to the Burn Service and I received little administrative support from the Department of Surgery. Many of my associates criticized me for taking on "those" patients. Beyond that, I soon came to experience the fact that despite all these difficulties, I was successful in treating patients with serious burns; but they left the hospital with "hollow" eyes, as if they were "dead" inside. The thought kept coming to me, "What am I doing to these poor patients?" I was putting them through a great deal of pain and agony, anxiety, stressful dressing changes and surgeries; and for what? They were leaving with feelings of fear of going back into society. Many asked me to let them die. Some who survived told me they wished they had died! I felt like a failure in spite of my 'statistics.' This could not be what God was calling me to do.

Even though the patients were being treated successfully, they did not want to go back into society. They were afraid that people would stare at them and gasp at their sight. They somehow felt ashamed of how they looked. They seemed to lose their self-respect and dignity. They had little or no expectations of future happiness. They realized what we all know; that when you are different from "normal," society makes you feel as though you are "bad" and no one wants to be around you. Burn victims are, in a sense, like the lepers in Scripture who had to "muffle their beards and shout unclean" whenever someone approached them. Adding all of these stresses together and, at the same time, my Church failing to give me the answers I desperately needed to help me through these crises, I began to think about leaving the Catholic Church and seeking God's grace somewhere else. I had reached the nadir of my religious life and I was near panic. One solution seemed best; to quit the Burn Unit. I had never quit anything I had made a commitment to do. I could not live with myself if I quit and I could not bear continuing doing what seemed to be futile and hopeless. I felt like Job sitting on the dung heap in despair.

It was at exactly that moment in my life that God called me to a personal encounter with His Son. That three-day encounter with Jesus has directed both my spiritual journey and my vision for the Burn Unit from that time forward. This encounter was the result of a strange and wonderful series of "coincidences" that began approximately five years previously in North Andover, Massachusetts, when Mary and I were godparents for my younger sister Anita's second child. As an aside, let me tell you that I do not believe in coincidences; they are little miracles arranged by God that often go unnoticed. The priest, Fr. Flagg, suggested that I make a three-day weekend retreat, called Cursillo. When I asked him what this weekend was about, he said "I can't explain it; you just have to experience it. Just DO it!! I had never heard of this retreat and I did not have any idea of how to find out how to get involved. About five years later, during a chance encounter with a friend during an Indian Guides' meeting with my younger son, Gregory, I met someone who sponsored me to the three-day weekend that changed my life.

"Cursillo de Christiandad" is a Spanish term meaning a short course in living what is fundamental for being Christian. The weekend teaches how to develop a personal relationship with Jesus through daily prayer and study in order to help the committed Christian develop an attitude aimed at being a missionary for Christ; that is, to live the mission of the Church as an apostle in the modern world. As a part of the Mystical Body of Christ, we are to live the mission of Jesus as priest, prophet and king. As priest—being for others a facilitator of a personal, living, loving relationship with God. As prophet—to witness to the life in the grace of God's love by the example of how we live our lives. As king—to be a servant to those in need and those who seek to find God's peace and consolation. His kingship is best illustrated in the passage when Jesus washes the feet of the disciples the night before He died.

This experience fit so precisely my recurring vision for my life. I learned so many basic truths about myself and about my God. One really important thing I came to understand was there are, in reality, three aspects or zones in each of our lives. First is the zone of "my responsibility." This zone includes all of the environments of my life— home, work, parish, social and professional organizations and my neighborhood. Within these environments I can choose to assume the responsibility for shaping the way I live in order to be an example to others, of life lived as a committed Christian. If this zone were pictured as a circle, it would have, at its center, the value system I would choose to live. I try to make "my" circle revolve around an axis of Christian values, forgiveness, sharing with others, affirming others for their goodness, accepting others as they are, lived as witness within each of those environments in order to proclaim the presence of God's Spirit among the people in that environment.

The second zone can be characterized as the zone of my life arranged by "Providence." These are events, anticipated or unanticipated, circumstances, situations, adversities, difficulties and "good luck." If this circle is to revolve around a Christian axis, it means that committed Christians should see each of the events in their life, including those perceived as good and those perceived as not so good, to be a revelation of God's plan for us. If our commitment to the Christian life is strong enough, difficulties we encounter do not turn us away and alter our Christian axis. The events that are life giving are perceived as gifts from God and the difficulties are perceived as events to be used to strengthen us, not to punish us.

The third is the zone of my own "control." This zone contains the part of my life devoted to building my life in grace through prayer and study and through the action of the witness I proclaim by the way I live my life. This zone takes on several attitudes of life. The first is *idealism,* which is the ability to see everything that happens in life as a manifestation of God's plan, therefore to seek the good in every situation or circumstance. The second is called *self-surrender*, that is the willingness to serve others for their benefit and to control the instinctual urge of self-preservation and 'taking care of number one.' It is the giving away of self; our time, our talent and our treasure, for the sake of others. The third is a *spirit of charity*. It is, in reality, interacting with others in your life in a loving, forgiving and caring manner, helping them bear their burdens and troubles with the aim of helping them see the virtue for *them* to live a life filled with the grace of God. It is helping others experience God's unconditional love for them by loving them unconditionally!

When each of these three zones is pictured as a circle revolving around an axis, the goal is to have each of these zones revolve around the same axis. As each of the zones becomes centered on the same axis, the circles begin to overlap each other. The more they share a common axis, the more they superimpose each other and have one common center. If each zone is centered on living Christian Values, then *every* part of life becomes an example of Christ alive in the world. As we strive to make every aspect of our life revolve around a Christian axis, we begin to experience what is termed "living the *Life in Grace*." That life is apostolic, that is, it invites people to accept God's love for them, not by our words but rather through our example. It is this goal, to be pursued as a vision for our life which is taught to us on the Cursillo weekend. Accepting these challenges can lead to a powerful change in attitudes and a re-ordering of life's priorities.

Perhaps the best description of what the Cursillo attempts to teach is summarized in Mark 2, 1-11. This is the story of the paralyzed man brought to Jesus by four friends. Because of the crowd pressing in upon Jesus, they were unable to get their friend close to Him to receive His blessing. They cut a hole in the roof and lowered the man down on a mat into Jesus' presence. Upon seeing how much faith his friends had, Jesus said to the paralyzed man, "I tell you, get up, pick up your mat and go home." Christians wishing to have an apostolic thrust in their life seek above all to be one of the four men who brought their friend to Jesus. In reality, it was their faith in the Lord manifested by their love for their friend that caused them to go "out of their way" for him, that saved the paralyzed man. We do not know whether the paralyzed man had faith himself, but Jesus saw the faith of his friends. Their love is what "saved" the paralyzed man.

The Life in Grace is the willingness to act as an instrument by which people are brought close to

Jesus. It facilitates their faith through the redemptive forgiveness that Jesus offers each of us. The life of such a Christian may not always be easy, but it is always fulfilling so long as we have the courage to continue to strive to manifest an apostolic thrust in our lives. To help us persevere, the Cursillo invites us to form communities in each of our environments in order to witness to the strength, power and transforming love that are the result from living the Life in Grace. It is this philosophy of life that became the foundation for the approach I took in forming the Burn Unit into what it was to become.

The revelation of what I experienced on that weekend showed me the possibilities of what my life could become. It transfixed my attention away from all of the problems I had brought to the weekend, and started me on a journey to find the proper way to implement an apostolic thrust to my life. The course also encourages us to form small communities of prayer and sharing. This 'reunion' of three or four friends is to meet weekly in order to help each other persevere in our life in God's grace. I was privileged to become a member of such a group. My brothers in Christ include a computer expert, an accountant and an ordained brother in the Blessed Sacrament Community. We pray together each Saturday morning, sharing the successes and failures of our life in grace, and helping each other re-commit ourselves to our goal of serving God through the witness of our lives. My group continues to meet weekly more than 30 years later.

Perhaps I should explain what I learned about prayer. It is a two-way conversation with God. When I am able to shed all the cares and concerns of my daily life and focus on the true inner self, at the very core of my being, the thoughts and words that form in my mind are, I believe, from God. I also came to believe that my response to God was not just in the words I say. My life, lived in a way that shares His message is, in fact, my response, my prayer to Him, lived out in the world. If only I could have all three zones of my life revolving around a Christian axis...a goal to strive for but never to be reached completely....

The Cursillo, for me, was a desert experience that gave me a chance to look within myself to search for the meaning of my life. Throughout the weekend those fateful words, "You are my beloved son," echoed through my head. Wow! I spent those three days pondering, "Is this real? Is this true? What am I supposed to do now?" I had to re-examine my goals. Would I continue to be self-centered? Would I seek after material wealth, power and fame? Would I continue to feel comfortable making God into my image and feeling righteous? After two days of intense soul-searching I found myself in a small chapel with a rough-cut wooden altar, a small crucifix and a single, tiny flickering candle. It was at that point that I gave myself to Him in a solemn moment of prayer; and life has never been the same.

When I asked Him how to serve Him more completely, the words that came into my head were terrifying: "*You* must love your family, your friends and your patients to life." My initial response was, "Yes," to family and friends. They are not very difficult to love. Love the patients? Not possible! Their needs are overwhelming! My experience showed me they were often angry and very difficult to deal with. They made me feel like it was my fault that they were suffering so much pain and anxiety. In their fright, they lashed out at everyone around them. They had lost their dignity and self-respect! Many felt ashamed of the way they looked, horribly different from what they looked like before. In reality, they were totally "dehumanized" and felt "unlovable" and "monstrous" as a result of their burn injuries. I asked God, "What does it mean to love them." Please God, do not ask me to love these ungrateful patients. I remember repeating to myself, "I can't. I can't. They need too much; much more than I can give." My medical and surgical skills were not sufficient to respond to these incredible needs. Dear God, "What was I to do?"

Over the next several weeks, with much prayer and "soul searching" I realized my mother had heard the same call; to reach out to those in need regardless of the personal cost. And she had said, "Yes!" Mom's courage helped me find great strength. I could not get her "message" out of my mind. She wanted me to give the same response she gave when asked how she had raised such a wonderful family. "I just loved them to life." While it would take almost a year for me to finally put my response into action, little did I realize the plan He was about to implement in my life.

SIX

Power of Love

"Greater love has no man than this, that a man lay down his life for his friends." John 15: 13

A midst all the turmoil in my life that was occurring at this time, a rather strange thing happened to me. My youngest sister Mary Joy, who is a Sister of the Humility of Mary Order, gave me a Bible written with alternate lines in Greek and English. When she gave it to me I asked her what was I to do with this book; she really did not know, but "something told her" that I should have this Bible. I had never studied Greek and I knew nothing of the language; so I took it with an inquisitive mind because I felt that there must be something I was to learn from this particular book. True enough. As I read some of my favorite passages in English, I became aware that the Greeks translated the word, "love," in three different ways. Sometimes the word was *eros* as in the "love of money is the root of all evil." When Jesus encountered the apostles on the shore of the Sea of Galilee, while cooking fish for them, following the resurrection, He took Peter aside and said, "Do you love me? Feed my sheep." The third time he asked the question, "Do you love me?" the word was *philos*. And in the passage, "greater love than this no man hath than to lay down his life for his friends," the word was *agapé*. This set in motion significant study on my part to understand what each of these translations meant. I was particularly intrigued because the word, "love," is used in so many ways in our modern society. For most people it signifies liking a lot, as in "I like vanilla ice cream but I just love chocolate." For others, it means "being in love."

What developed was an understanding that these three words described levels of relationships between individuals. A relationship at the *eros* level is characterized by love of self, that is, the relationship is for the benefit of "self" at the expense of the "other" in the relationship. It is the sensual part of a love relationship. It is living by our instincts—the prime instinct of self-preservation and using others for self-gratification. People living erotic relationships dominate others in order to feel important and to satisfy needs of self at the expense of the needs of others. It means being willing to use others for personal gain and/or satisfaction. It is characterized as loving things and using people! This kind of relationship tends to be destructive since it is totally self-centered and bears little true value to the other person in the relationship, who is often victimized! It can be equated to a 'pagan' level of relationship.

I have come to understand *philos* as human love. That is the love between individuals in which the relationship is characterized by doing good things for each other and tolerating each other's faults for the mutual benefit of the relationship; as in good marriages, good neighbors and good friends. It is deep friendship at a human level; "I'll be nice to you as long as you are nice to me." These relationships can be mutually beneficial and lead to happy and fulfilling lives. However, since these relationships are dependent on the continued commitment to the relationship by both parties, the relationship can dissolve when one party feels aggrieved by the other for some reason. Often times the relationship is broken or destroyed when one party simply walks away for personal reasons because it is not perceived as being beneficial enough to either of the parties. It can be great while it lasts, but it may not last. Marriages on this level often end in divorce.

The third level of a love relationship is *agapé*. This level of love is supernatural; that is, it originates from God. It is love that is beyond human capacity and is not possible unless a person is inspired by the love God has for the individual. I believe Grace can be defined as *God's Transforming Love*. For me, that is the definition of *agapé* love. I have come to understand that this is the love that God has for every one of us because I have experienced that love. It is unconditional and constant. It is forgiving our transgressions and affirming to us for our goodness in spite of the selfish things we do (sin). Nothing we can do can interrupt this love for us!

As I struggled to understand, as best I could, what this relationship really meant, I was struck by the awareness that Jesus came to live with us on earth so we might experience what *agapé* love really is. It can not be taught, it must be experienced; and once it is experienced, it can be passed on to one another. In fact, in my mind, that *was* His message! His reason for coming to live among us was to give each of us an example of *how* to live unconditional love relationships with each other. This love is not just a feeling or emotion. It is an action word, a verb. It requires that the lover do something to build a relationship based upon sacrificial and unconditional love for others, especially those with greatest needs. In life, names like Gandhi and Mother Teresa come to mind … and many others as well.

In reading the Scripture, it became clear to me that what He was teaching us was, that in order to have an *agapé* relationship with another person, *we* have to accept others without judgment, just as they are, in all their brokenness and sinfulness. But first, we need to reconcile our personal lives so we do not carry burdens of guilt and shame for things we have done, or for things we did not do but should have. Every major faith and religion states clearly and with emphasis that our Creator is always ready to forgive us. We just need to believe that God loves us enough to set us free and give us the choice to either sin against others or to love one another. GOD HAS FAITH IN US!

His life was an example to us that when *we* love unconditionally, our relationships can not be broken by any act of the other person. It is sacrificial love in which the good of the beloved is more important than the good for the lover. It is the willingness to forgive others when they hurt *you*, and moreover, to turn the other cheek when they do. It is the willingness to help them bear their burdens, to be with them in time of trouble, to literally give them "the shirt off your back." It is to be concerned for the welfare of others before the concern for your own welfare.

Marriages built on this level of sacrificial love and commitment are truly inspiring. They survive all the difficulties that are a part of every long lasting relationship. Within the marriage bond, all three levels of love are present in proper perspective. There is a sensual relationship between husband and wife which binds them, physically into one person. The sexuality of both partners must be expressed in a wholesome manner, but should not be the dominant focus of the relationship. Likewise there is a human level of love which needs to be maintained in marriage. Each partner must remain a whole person with personal integrity, self-esteem and a sense of personal worth. When lived as a part of a wholesome *agapé* relationship, it personifies mutual respect and understanding of each other's differences. It does not imply one member needs to become the "door-mat" of the other as a sign of a sacrificial relationship! Giving away of "self" to the other partner does not mean losing that which makes you lovable in the eyes of your beloved! It means maintaining psychological boundaries between each other, lest one or both partners lose their sense of self and individual dignity.

Rather, the true unconditional loving relationship in marriage requires that each partner sees the other as gift, with all the differences between them as bridges to becoming more complete as individuals themselves, through each other's love. Each becomes a more complete person because of their partner and they truly grow to become one with each other! This is the ideal environment in which children should be nurtured. The loving relationship between parents will lead their children to feel safe and secure as they grow in self-assurance, dignity and self worth. The fruit of unconditional love is always new life for all involved!

Is that not exactly what Jesus told us? His life truly *was* the manifestation of how God loves us— each and every one—saint and sinner. Nothing we can do can ever separate us from this kind of love! Nothing. I believe sinfulness is freely and knowingly choosing NOT to love and instead, choosing to be self-seeking in all things. All any of us sinners needs to do is ask for forgiveness for our transgressions and recommit ourselves to love each other, and God forgives us and "wipes the slate clean." Those of *us* who are willing to commit ourselves to live that level of love become witnesses to God's unconditional love for every person. We become "apostles in the modern world."

It is not easy but it is possible. A relationship at that level must satisfy three truths. First, this level of love must be freely given and freely accepted; it can not be coerced. I can not make someone love me nor can I force someone to accept my love. It must be voluntarily given and voluntarily received. Second, it always transforms both the lover and the beloved to a new level of happiness in life and a greater sense of peace and joy in the depths of our being. Since these relationships are manifestations of God's love for us, the presence of His Spirit is present in this love relationship, and that makes the relationship *transcendent*. Third, it always makes the lover vulnerable to the beloved. Love at this level can not be canceled, no matter how the beloved responds. Should the beloved walk away, *agapé* love endures in the hope that the beloved will return to the relationship. The story of the Prodigal Son is a perfect reflection of this level of relationship. The father loved his younger son enough to let him go, even though he knew his son would likely squander his inheritance and destroy his life; and yet the unconditional nature of his love for his son remained as strong as ever! The son was forced to work in a pigsty, the most humiliating work there could be for a Jew. Yet he knew his father would allow him to return because his father loved him unconditionally. This level of love relationship with another person can only be generated by faith that God loves each of us unconditionally. That and only that makes it possible for us to love our neighbors unconditionally. As ourselves!

Most of us are frightened at the prospect of entering into such a relationship. *Sacrificial* love requires that we become vulnerable to others and that always makes us uncomfortable. Therefore, such a decision requires a commitment of our will. Each of us has been given intelligence, reason and free will. Intelligence is the ability to "know." Reason is the ability to "think." Free Will is the ability to "choose." If we are to love unconditionally, we must use all these faculties and freely choose to live this life. As stated before, 'our free choices determine the life we lead.' No other single choice can have such a profound effect on our lives. This commitment needs constant nurturing through regular prayer and the study of Scripture and other good books. It must have constant reinforcement found primarily in an intimate, personal and loving relationship with God; for Christians, through His Son, Jesus.

As these truths became ingrained in my heart, I began to understand what God was calling me to do and who I was to become. My initial response that I could not love burn patients because they needed so much was exactly the thing that spurred me to the prayer and meditation that helped lead me to my current understanding of the word love. He filled the emptiness of my despair with a new found level of understanding. I also realized that I truly could not meet the needs of my family, my friends and certainly my patients by myself, because they truly did need more than I alone could give. It was then that I finally understood what I had been taught on my Cursillo weekend. I had to form a community in my Burn Unit environment just like in my home environment, in order to bring others together around an axis of Christian values and principles. The goal was to fill each environment, including the Burn Unit, with His peace, His consolation and His joy. Slowly, the answer to my question, "How do I live out an apostolic life?" became clear.

I began the process of building a "burn team"— a group of individuals, each with their own special expertise, but willing to relate to one another and to relate to the patients with a mindset centered on a Christian axis of values that reflected faith and trust in each other in order to demonstrate to patients and families that loving relationships were present for them and their loved one. Once my eyes were opened I began searching for individuals who would "buy into" this philosophy. The first to respond was a young physical therapist named

Sharon, who became committed to helping me care for burn patients. In the early days of the Burn Unit, we treated patients with the customary Hubbard Tank baths that were generally done each day in the Physical Therapy Department, except for the weekends when PT was closed. Many of the patients got into serious trouble between Friday and Monday because their dressings were not changed properly. Sharon, who became my first ally, volunteered to come in on the weekends to do the dressings on those patients who could not wait for Monday. Since the hospital had no provisions for overtime work by therapists, she was willing to come to the hospital on the weekends *without pay*! Her kind and generous act was met with rebuttal by the administration of the hospital. They said, correctly, she could not single-handedly manage a patient on a gurney, plus maneuver the patient in and out of the Hubbard Tank. They were worried that if a patient slipped off the gurney into the water she would be unable to get the patient out and there would be no one around to help her because the department was closed.

When I saw the depth of her commitment, I had no choice except to elect to help her myself on the weekends. We would bring the patients down from the floor; the guard would unlock the Physical Therapy Unit and lock the doors behind us. We would proceed with the tubbing and dressing change, then re-dress the patient, call the guard to let us out and bring the patient back to the floor. She would then return to the physical therapy suite to clean up and put everything in order for the following day. Her sacrifice was an incredibly generous and a voluntary witness of her faith. The result was an awareness that spread throughout the hospital personnel that there must be 'something special' going on in the Burn Unit for Sharon to be willing to do what she was doing every weekend without pay. It was an inspirational act of *agapé* love and it had a profound effect on many people in the hospital, especially me.

Shortly after this, two practical nurses, Evelyn and Georgine from the pediatric unit volunteered to help. They made an immediate impact on the care of patients since we cared for pediatric as well as adult patients on the Burn Service. The next to join the team was a registered nurse who moved from Toledo to Cleveland and came to work in the Unit. Jan was a true professional of incredible tal-

ent and energy. To this day, I have never met a better or more dedicated nurse even though I have
worked with many who are like her! She was truly
a gift from God. As head nurse, she took on the
responsibility of 'setting the tone' of the Burn Unit
environment by demonstrating the example of
compassionate care for our patients.

Because no house staff had been assigned to the
Burn Unit, all the patient care procedures such as
nasogastric tube placement, IV lines and urinary
catheters were my responsibility. I received permission to teach Jan these tasks despite the fact that
rules at that time prohibited nurses from doing
these things. Jan was a 'quick learn' and my life
became much more manageable after that. Of
course, that elevated Jan above all the other nurses
in the hospital because she could do things they
were not permitted to do. Other nurses soon volunteered to come to work in the Unit as a result.
They too were given the same privileges and within
several years, the Unit led the way so that all registered nurses in the hospital functioned at that level.

A short time later, another practical nurse,
Cathy, joined the Burn Unit staff. She was really
frightened at the prospect of working in the Burn

Unit because she had never worked in a hospital setting before. She was a most wonderful Christian young lady who had already experienced a Cursillo weekend. Together, with Sharon, Georgine, Evelyn, Jan and Cathy, the burn team "community" began to take shape. We formed a tandem to create an environment wherein we could articulate and demonstrate the principles of compassion in the care of these 'lepers' of the modern world—ugly, suffering and dehumanized burn patients.

We tried to explain to our co-workers the reasons why we cared for our patients the way we did, but it was difficult to give an understandable explanation. It was a different concept to what was accepted as 'normal.' The only thing I could tell them was "to come and see." It meant each of us leading by example, whatever our role was, as a witness of our faith. It helped others see this as a way for *them* to give care. Over the next year, many more health professionals joined us—social workers, occupational and physical therapists, a dietitian and child-care workers. The reputation of the Burn Unit began to spread beyond the hospital.

The "team" began to give total patient care that revolved around the Christian axis of *agapé* love.

Not everyone was a Christian, but all adopted that philosophy and work ethic. From that time on, health care professionals of every department have consistently come forward and volunteered to work on the Unit. Recruitment has never been a problem. As a matter of fact, a number of nurses, therapists and social workers waited for years, until there was an opening to join our team. Our current head nurse has been part of the Unit for 26 years and our assistant head nurse more than 16 years. Their loyalty and dedication reflect the real values we all try to practice. No obstacle or seemingly insurmountable problem will make us quit!

Our team came together with a stronger and stronger bond between us. We were forming ourselves into a community. We were able to trust each other with our feelings and shared problems revolving around patient-care issues. We learned we could solve problems best by working through consensus and it gave us a good climate in which to work. We recognized that it was not only the expert care we gave our patients, but moreover, it was the way the care was given and the environment in which it was delivered that had the most profound effect upon the total, "interior" recovery our patients were experiencing. We knew that burns occur from the *outside in,* but we learned that total recovery of burn patients occurs from the *inside out.* The job we had set out to accomplish was, in reality, much bigger than we thought. Rather than overwhelming us, it forced us to rely more and more on each other. We were the ones who understood what we were trying to do, and therefore only we could do it. But we needed each other to be successful! We formed ourselves into a family!

It soon became apparent that what I had seen in the patients in the early days of the Burn Unit, when patients left the Unit with a dead expression in their eyes, was true enough. It really was a reflection of their lack of a sense of dignity and self-esteem coupled with feelings of guilt and anger. Their injury and their scars in fact, totally dehumanized them. God's transforming love, through the dedicated relationships of the burn team members put into action with our patients, began to have a profound effect on the patients as they went through their recovery. I saw a dramatic increase in self-respect developing within many patients. They were treated with dignity and as a result felt a greater sense of dignity develop within themselves.

They began to recognize that their self-esteem was returning and they were able to accept the fact that life after burns was possible for them. They began to believe their scars could not take away their inner beauty.

At the same time I began to see the effects of our burn team on the families of the burn patients. We were able to help them understand more fully and accept with more grace the terrible tragedy that happened to their loved ones. They began to see the virtue in the way the staff was caring for them and they also began to understand how their loved ones could regain their dignity and self-esteem in spite of their scars. I recognized that it was a spirit of transforming love that was coming to life in the Burn Unit through the members of the burn team.

Our burn team is like an extended family. Like any good family, we multiply the joy of our successes and divide the sorrow we encounter when we lose a patient. In doing these things, we find strength and courage to persevere when the work load seems overpowering or patients are not doing as well as we would like. Practicing as a family fosters relationships which bind us together as a health care team of professionals. It is the axis of values around which this environment revolves that keeps us focused on our patients and their families. This value system is at the heart of what we do and, moreover, how we do it. In reality, we were only just beginning to function like the team we would become. The power of a healing spirit was coming to life in our Unit!

Life in Grace

*"There is a young lad here with five loaves
and three fish." John 12*

O
ne of the most valuable things I discovered
in the study of the Scriptures was to put
myself into the Bible story and reflect on
which person I am in each of the Gospel passages.
What I found was that it made the Gospel passages
real for me in today's world rather than as events
that happened two thousand years ago. The problems that Jesus addresses are the same problems we
have in the world today and I have in my own life
today. One of the key passages that helped me, perhaps as much as any, is the story of the loaves and
fishes. The version most helpful to me is written by
St. John. Sometimes when I read this passage I am

one of the Pharisees or Sadducees, trying to figure out, in an intellectual way, exactly what happened on that wonderful afternoon. Sometimes I feel like one of the crowd, looking for answers and trying to figure out, "Is Jesus for real and does He have the answers for me?" Sometimes I'm Andrew, the apostle who continuously brings people to Jesus; and sometimes I'm Philip, full of doubt that God, through Jesus, can accomplish the great task of teaching us the keys of the kingdom. I might add here that when Peter told Jesus that He was the Messiah, the Son of God, and Jesus said, "I give you the keys of the kingdom," that Jesus is saying to each one of us who acknowledges that He is the Messiah and the Son of God that we possess the keys of the kingdom as well. With that thought in mind, I want most of all, to be the boy with the loaves and fishes.

Visualize if you will, the hillside covered with men and women who have been listening to Jesus preach and it is now past time to eat. Andrew comes forward and tells Jesus there is a lad with several loaves and fishes. While the Scripture does not explicitly tell us, it seems logical to me to visualize that Jesus would have asked Andrew to bring the boy to Him. My understanding of the Jewish tradition is that when a boy reaches twelve and makes his Bar Mitzvah, he is then a man. Therefore, the young lad must be ten or eleven. Why would he be carrying loaves and fishes? Probably his mother packed his lunch, which suggests he had come a long way to hear Jesus. Consider that Jesus probably said something like, "Son would you like to share your loaves and fishes with my friends?" Now the boy, although immature, possesses intelligence, reason and free will. He must have been stunned to look at his basket with a few loaves and fishes and look up at the hillside and see this mass of people. He probably thought, my goodness, this guy must be crazy! Or he might have thought, well, gee, if I give my food away I will not have anything to eat on the way home. *He had the freedom to say, "No."* And if he had said, "No," there would have been no miracle because I am quite sure that Jesus would not have forcibly taken the loaves and fishes from the boy. I believe this Gospel illustrates clearly that for the will of God to be completed on earth, we must, using our intelligence, reason and free will, make a decision to say "Yes" to His invitation to share our "loaves and fishes."

Each of us has a "basket of loaves and fishes" which are in reality the gifts and talents that God has given each of us, gifts that make everyone a unique individual. All of us have special gifts and talents, freely given to us by God, which no other person ever created or ever to be created will have in exactly the same qualities or proportion. Our basket also contains weaknesses that God, through His Providence, has given us to help us learn to be dependent on God so we can overcome those weaknesses by applying our gifts of strengths and talents.

God makes each of us unique. He gives each of us a tiny piece of Himself. This means to me that God's wonderful creation, the entire universe, is incomplete without you and me! Each day God is asking us that penetrating question, "Will you share your gifts and talents and all your strengths and weaknesses with my friends?" That is a prerequisite question for anyone who attempts to live in union with God. By using our intelligence, reason and free will, if we say, "Yes," *miracles do happen*. I do not equate miracles with magic. Miracles do not have to be something that defies God's perfect plan of creation. Miracles do not require lightning bolts. I believe miracles happen whenever *sacrificial* love is practiced. The beloved person is able to increase self-esteem and dignity, become more fully alive, and achieve a higher level of inner peace and tranquility. Miracles happen when people find a direction in their life that they have been searching for but have been unable to find. Miracles happen whenever individuals, through faith, are willing to live the loving, unconditional relationship with each other, because that always transforms both the lover and the beloved to a newness of life and a more complete sense of peace and justice.

God is always at work in the heart of every Christian and the "fallout" is the wonderful things that happen as a result; that is, the transformation of the small "world" of that Christian and the people who are part of that world. The greater the "fallout" the more energized the Christian becomes. The increased spirituality that results is then given away more completely and there is more "fallout." Try it. It really works. *This is the life-style of a saint!* It is the secret of a beautiful life. It is called true happiness. I have seen it happen. I have seen it happen many times. I have experienced the joy of being a tiny instrument that God uses to transform the lives of others through His overpowering grace; and my heart is filled with a greater and greater sense of the mystery and power that God's love has when it is unleashed into the world. Living the life in grace is not difficult. He told us that His burden is easy, and it is, if we concentrate on the supernatural gifts we have been given—faith, hope and love. However, if we concentrate on the human aspects of what it is He is asking us to do, it can become a burden because helping others at the sacrifice of self is a *heavy* duty when it is not done in a spiritual sense. It brings resentment when we *have* to do something for somebody else or when we *have* to accept the fact that someone dear to us has hurt us. It is a burden when we *have* to feel the obligation to forgive them when they hurt us and our human nature cries out with everything that we possess, "No I can not forgive such a grievous act."

As Paul so elegantly describes in his Letter to the Romans, we are constantly at war between our human nature and our spiritual nature. Paul refers to our human nature as "the law" which means living by external constraints that we do not sincerely embrace or understand. He contrasts this with our spiritual nature, which is to live as Christ calls us to live. Our human nature tends to be self-serving and is more comfortable with selfish relationships as opposed to following the teachings of Jesus and living in a spiritual, loving sense. I believe that God created us in exactly that way and intended for us to be faced with this challenge and conflict. It is in overcoming our human nature, which is the life led by instincts of self-preservation and self-aggrandizement, that we truly can appreciate the power of our spiritual nature. *We must have the capacity to choose to sin in order to gain the rewards for choosing not to sin, but to live in grace.* If we have no choice but to be virtuous, what will that gain for us? We can not have the choice of seeking Heaven if we do not have the choice of choosing Hell.

The conflict is continuous within each of us throughout our lives. Clearly, in order for me to live a life in grace, it must be a decision of my will. I believe that is why we must continuously "breathe in" prayer and study to fortify ourselves lest we give in to the temptation of reverting to our human condition and become selfish and self-centered. The "breathing out" is apostolic action. This prophetic action is either by word or witness. Most of us are not good "preachers." Besides, telling people what they should or should not do usually turns them off, almost all the time. We can proclaim our faith by witnessing to each other, that is, by the example of how we live our lives. Actions do speak louder than words. We can not fake what we do.

I have learned how difficult it is to maintain a balance in life between meeting my human needs and living a life in grace. The power I receive to try to persevere comes from the positive reinforcement I receive from those who love me and from those who, by the power of God's love for them, overcome their human limitations and transcend their human condition to do unbelievable things in spite of handicaps, tragedy and triumphs. First and foremost, I am constantly renewed by the love that Mary and my family have for me, in spite of the selfish things I do (sins). By their willingness to forgive me over and over again, they are the clearest image I have of God's love for me.

Another important support is what I receive from my prayer group as we come together weekly to share our lives in grace and help each other persevere in our apostolic endeavors. When I am unable to make the weekly meetings, there is a void that I feel until I meet with my brothers in Christ again. An additional continuing source of inspiration comes from the members of the burn team, along with the patients and their families as they witness to the transcendent power of the human spirit.

I have become so dependent on the inspiration I receive from those who love me and work with me that I believe, with all my heart, that *an isolated Christian is a paralyzed Christian.* While it is theoretically possible to persevere in the life in grace as an individual, the burden of finding the strength to recommit to that life on a daily basis is almost certainly beyond the reach of most of us if we try to do it by ourselves. I believe that is why we are called to live in community with those who share our Inner Life.

The awareness that I, in some small way, have been an instrument used by God in the remarkable transformation in the lives of others is truly the power that helps me persevere in my desire to be of service to others. All we need to keep in mind is the sacrifice that Jesus made for others throughout His life, culminating in the great sacrifice of His life for us on the cross. I do not concentrate on the

pain and suffering that Jesus endured in the crucifixion, even though it was incredible. I concentrate, rather, on the depth of love He had for us
that allowed Him to make a free choice to *willingly*
stretch out His hands on the cross. *I believe with all
my heart that if I were the only person ever created,
Jesus would have come and died for me.*

He told us that love never dies and that love can
conquer every problem in the minds and hearts of
those who follow Him. Lives can end in death, but
loving relationships last forever. This is what I told
my father as he lay dying in the hospital on his last
Christmas Eve. I learned it when my Dad faced his
death with grace and dignity! I have seen that
power unleashed in my life in many, many small
and seemingly insignificant ways. When I reflect
on the events of each day in my evening prayer, I
become aware that His hand has been at work in
all those small and seemingly insignificant events.
I find myself reciting over and over, "Thou art
great and Thou art good, Lord. All creation rightly
gives You thanks and praise."

EIGHT

Spirituality of Suffering

"I am the Way, the Truth and the Life." John 14: 6

Each of us has, in our mind's eye, a view concerning what is referred to as suffering. For some of us, it is a personal experience, or it may be an empathetic response to the perceived pain or suffering of a loved one or friend. It may be the physical suffering of pain or infirmity, either acute or chronic; for others it may be the debilitating effects of chemotherapy or other invasive or intrusive therapies. It may be in the form of mental anguish over situations that can not be altered or controlled; it may be in the form of relationships that have become hurtful and distorted; or, for others, it could simply be fear of the future when they face the foreboding prospect of death.

For Christians, suffering is embodied in the crucifixion of Jesus. We believe in the redemptive value of suffering, but let me say at the outset that I do not believe that suffering for the sake of suffering in order to expiate our sins is what is meant by this concept. Suffering can focus our thoughts and prayers to help us become more dependent on God's interventions and less dependent on our own personal control of whatever the situation is that is causing the suffering. It is the thousands of burn patients I have cared for over the last 30 years who have taught me the qualities of suffering and the spiritual values that I have learned through their suffering. Therefore, in order for you to understand my perspective on suffering, you will need to enter my world, the Burn Unit, for a brief moment.

Come with me as I respond to the pager, notifying me of a young man who has been involved in a propane explosion at work and who has been brought to our trauma bay. As we approach the room, we can smell the acrid odor of smoke and burned flesh. We see firefighters covered with soot and the trauma team dressed in gowns, masks, hoods, boots and gloves scurrying to save the patient's life. As we approach the bedside, we see that his face is badly burned and that a breathing tube has been placed in his lungs, making it possible for him to breathe but making it impossible for him to speak. We look into his eyes and we see fear, anxiety and pain. He can not talk, but he communicates the way he is feeling quite effectively. Three quarters of his body has been burned and he is being rapidly assessed for other injuries that could have occurred in the explosion. The medical student at my side inquires about his survival, and I remind her that while it is probable, it will take the combined skill of many dedicated and highly trained medical professionals working together as a team to save his life and return him to his family.

The next four hours pass in a blur as we start the intravenous lines to stabilize this patient's blood pressure and perform the life-saving measures that will help him survive. As the initial hectic response is completed, the student and I go out to the waiting room to encounter his wife, nervously twisting a handkerchief awaiting word of her husband's condition. The glazed look in her eyes tells me that she can not truly understand anything I am trying to tell her. All she wants to hear is that he is going to be all right. While I can not promise success, I do promise that we will do our best to save him, and that we will help her cope with the rigors of the next six critical weeks. Perhaps the most important thing I say is that I will never abandon her husband or her. One of our social workers/counselors and our chaplain come in to sit with her and comfort her. They reassure her that her loved one will receive the finest care possible from our very dedicated and experienced burn team professionals. They sit with her quietly, and slowly she is able to express to them her deepest fears and concerns. Together, they end the session by praying for strength and courage.

The weeks that follow are a blur of activity; dressing changes, IV's, multiple surgical procedures, blood transfusions, tube feedings antibiotics and other life-saving interventions. A pattern unfolds that is common to most patients in this situation. The physical suffering is incredible. Constant administration of morphine, tranquilizers and sedatives only dull the pain and anxiety, even though high doses of these drugs are given intravenously, as a continuous infusion.

A burn injury of this magnitude stresses the human body beyond that of any other disease or

injury. Every major organ system becomes dysfunctional and requires close attention and rapid
therapeutic interventions to control for organ failure. As a result, in a physical sense, the body is
totally vulnerable to multi-organ failure, infection,
septic syndrome and death. Moreover, members
of the burn team inflict much of the pain experienced by burn patients. Changing dressings,
scrubbing wounds and exercising joints are
painful but necessary parts of the daily routine.
Regardless of empathy on the part of the staff, the
suffering of patients is exaggerated by the treatments they must endure. The toxic effects of the
drugs make patients' minds dysfunctional. They
can not differentiate between dreams and reality
and often relate stories that they relive the agony
of the fire over and over again as their treatments
are administered.

Intellectually, it is impossible for patients to fully
understand everything that is happening to them or
the reasons why things must be done that are so
painful, particularly dressing changes. The reality
they see is an ugly distortion of their body. When
they see the injured parts of their bodies, they do
not recognize themselves . . . that can not be me!

Families have a difficult time recognizing their loved ones through the burns and bandages. No amount of explanation, no matter how basic, can help patients or families fully understand what is happening. They just want it to stop. Now! In the beginning, it is difficult for patients to trust us when we say they must undergo their rigorous daily routines. It is at these times that many patients ask us to let them die.

Their emotional response to the reality of their situation and the ugliness they see in themselves leads many patients to develop a foreboding fear of survival because they fear they will be so badly scarred and disfigured. They know they will be subject to stares, whispers and ridicule. They soon realize that people who are "different" are judged to be less than equal. Society has a way of making individuals who are different from "normal" feel as if they are "bad." This fear is especially evident when exposed parts of the body—face, hands, neck—are badly burned. Many patients fear their survival more than death itself. We developed a special program that we institute when we think patients are ready, and when they agree to see their facial burns for the first time. We try to have family available. Also our primary nurse and social service counselor are present. Until then, we avoid any casual opportunity for patients to see themselves by keeping mirrors out of their sight. Seeing themselves is often an overpowering experience they never quite forget!

Some patients are able to express their feelings about their relationship with God, who becomes very important to them in their distress. The reality of their situation causes them to reflect on their past deeds and/or misdeeds. Patients have expressed the idea that God is actually angry with them for past indiscretions. They feel guilty for things they may have done, or for things they should have done but chose not to do. For many, there is a reaction of guilt and shame. Keep in mind that fire is taken as the sign of God's damnation. Many patients have told me they believe that God is punishing them and has turned away from them. They can not accept the notion that God loves them. Many patients have told me, "No one could love me the way I am." They project their ugly feelings about themselves to others including God, and what is reflected back to them is destructive to their inner selves, their very souls.

What I have described to you is the total disintegration of the human person. Burn injuries alter the four facets of personhood—physical, intellectual, emotional and spiritual. All are deformed and dysfunctional. This total loss of self-respect, dignity and self-esteem is, to me, the ultimate form of suffering that can befall a human being.

Most of us wear "masks" which help us to show others only those qualities we wish them to see about us and hide the blemishes or character faults that we wish others not to see. We choose carefully those people to whom we entrust our deepest feelings and fears. We are uncomfortable when we feel vulnerable and, in fact, the masks we hide behind may actually lead to self-deception, as we perceive ourselves as something we truly are not. Keeping these masks in place requires a great deal of intellectual and emotional energy. When patients are faced with overwhelming destruction of their self-esteem and dignity as we see in our patients, there is not enough energy left to hide behind and the masks come down. All the beautiful veneer is stripped away and patients and their families are brought face to face with reality.

Individuals in this state frequently develop

pathological and self-destructive coping mechanisms to deal with this feeling of vulnerability to others. They have projected their feelings of ugliness and worthlessness into the world and that is what is reflected back to them. The world looks ugly and frightening to them. This reaction can be described as building a wall to keep others out while they retreat into a state of withdrawal and depression. I have had many, many patients plead with me to let them die. They can not envision living in that state.

When I first began working in the Burn Unit, I was overwhelmed with my sense of failure. Despite good surgical training and skill at taking care of life-threatening burns, applying skin grafts and reconstructing burn scars, it became clear to me that the loss of self-respect, dignity and self-esteem prevented patients from returning to a meaningful, fulfilling and happy life. I became aware that trying to *cure* their burn injuries was not possible. Even though their burn injury is not a terminal illness, it is incurable; the scars are "forever." The patients needed to be *healed*. I also realized that healing is a process that goes on for the rest of their lives. I realized that these patients needed to feel whole but their needs were so great I could not do it by myself. I had to be brought to a state where I was overwhelmed with a sense of my own personal hopelessness before I could see their suffering from a spiritual perspective. Out of my own my despair, I first began to experience the spirituality of suffering.

I define healing as the bringing together the four parts of our personhood into a state of balance. Balance is the key, not perfection, because not one of us can be perfect; we all have faults and weaknesses of mind, body or spirit, that sometimes seem insurmountable. We can, however accept what we can't change, change what we can and learn to live in peace with the imperfections we have to live with. No matter how flawed any one is, including people with life threatening burns, healing of mind, body and spirit is possible and can bring our damaged personhood into a balance of self-acceptance and inner peace. I know this is possible. I have witnessed many examples in my career.

There lies within each individual the capacity to transcend our human condition through the power of God's transforming love to bring about true healing of mind, body and spirit. Buddhism states, as one of its tenets, that a person must be totally empty before transcendence is possible. I believe that my patients do, in fact, become totally empty; devoid of the ability to hide behind the masks of self-deception and wishful thinking. They are brought face-to-face with their loss of personhood. What patients reveal to me can be summarized as feeling monstrous and unlovable. It is at that terrifying moment that healing can begin.

My faith tells me that the only way people who feel unlovable can change their perception of self is to experience the transforming love of God's grace. Remember, sacrificial love can not be taught or learned. It must be experienced. This love is not an experience of the mind but of the heart. Once it has been experienced, and only then, can it be passed on to others. The Great Commandment states that we should love God with all our heart, with all our strength and with all our mind; and our neighbor as ourselves. Most of us do not have the coping skills to find these elusive answers when we are in a state of total collapse, but the Great Commandment gives us a blue print to follow. Let me remind you that there are three persons in this commandment—God, neighbor and self. When people feel alienated from God, they are unable to appreciate a meaningful relationship with Him, particularly if they think that God is punishing them for some reason. Love of self in the commandment is not the narcissistic view of self, but the realistic self-awareness that comes through humility in recognizing our own God-given strengths and limitations. Love of self is self-respect, dignity and self-esteem. They are free gifts from our God Who loves us and calls us to use those gifts for our happiness and His glory.

Since many of my patients feel alienated from God and lack the coping skills necessary to deal with the overwhelming deprivation they are experiencing, there is only one solution to the problem. That is love of neighbor. The opportunity to be healed under these circumstances requires that the patients relate to those people they can see and hear and touch as the example of God's love for them. As the Chinese so aptly define it, the word for crisis embodies both danger and opportunity. The danger is that the self-destructive loss of personhood will lead patients to despair; and in their despair, turn away from the very power that can heal them. In the case of our patients, it meant the burn team had the opportunity of helping them feel the healing compassion and empathy they so desperately needed. That experience could give them the chance to realize they really were loved by their Creator through the caring of their neighbors. For us caregivers, it meant accepting them as they were, forgiving them for the cursing and kicking and biting and all which hurt us, helping them carry their burdens of pain and suffering with compassion, turning the other cheek when necessary and affirming our patients for their goodness in spite of their hurtful actions. It is, in short, witnessing to unbound love. On a human level this may be called crisis intervention; on a spiritual level it is the beginning of healing and transcendence.

As it became clearer and clearer to me that I could not respond adequately to my patients' total needs as an individual, I knew I would need a community of like-minded health professionals to work together as a T.E.A.M. (That became our motto; *Together Each Accomplishes More*). The burn T.E.A.M. community is a living thing and like all living things, it is either growing or dying; life never stays the same. As the leader of the burn team I found it necessary throughout the marvelous growth that I had witnessed within the members of the team that I continue to be able to provide the leadership that keeps the team members centered on the Christian axis of love. Through the years, therefore, it became imperative that I continue to practice the "breathing in" function of prayer and study in order to continue the "breathing out" function necessary to maintain the apostolic drive to continuously call the members of the burn team to our mission.

Our team is not a hierarchy. Each member has a role with different responsibilities, but each role is essential to the success of the team. Our team includes everyone working on the Unit; the professional staff plus the secretaries, nurse aides and housekeepers. We all share responsibilities for the ultimate care of our patients. Therefore, we all share in the team-building functions we celebrate—holiday dinners, picnics, lunches to mark special occasions and birthdays.

By having everyone participate, all felt a degree of ownership in the Unit. The pride of working in this environment enabled each caregiver to carry out their responsibilities beyond the minimum requirements. It became their Unit, not Dr. Frat's Unit, not the hospital's Burn Unit, but *their Unit*. They became invested in the success of what we were trying to accomplish; together, doing more and better as a team! This attitude also fostered a feeling of family within the group. There was not a lot complaining about the workload and staff members began volunteering to take on the most difficult and labor intensive patients.

The staff felt comfortable listening to patients' fears and anxieties with understanding and support. Our secretary, who was a black lady, was an invaluable team member because she could help our young black patients open up to the staff about their feelings and fears! What developed was an atmosphere of peace and joy and support amidst the agony and pain and suffering of the patients. My experience had taught me that the greatest force in helping others to accept themselves as being worthy to feel good about themselves is *affirmation*. Therefore the patients needed to be in the exact environment they were in. The affirmation and supportive encouragement they received rekindled within them a sense of dignity and personhood in spite of their suffering and perceived ugliness.

My job, as one who seeks to facilitate the expression of that spirit in the Burn Unit, is to mobilize the burn team into a community of individuals who center their professional lives on an axis that exemplifies the principles of Christian values. Though most, but not all, are Christian, they accept and espouse the principles in their own way and thus immerse the patients and the families in an environment that is nurturing and supportive. Of course, the first rule of medical care is that each team member must be competent. They must perform their individual duties properly because a severely burned patient is critically ill and in danger of death for many weeks. They can not tolerate any margin for error and therefore all caregivers must be focused and competent if these patients are to do well. The housekeeper had to be included in the team because unless the Unit is kept scrupulously clean, infection is more likely and patients will suffer more risks for serious complications.

But beyond that, it is the way we practice our expertise that helps patients regain self-esteem. It is not only *what* we do but also *how* we do it that makes a difference! Team members strive to be "present" to their patients. They do this by listening patiently to their fears and endless questions; by "turning the other cheek" when patients swear and scream and lash out at them; by praying with them when appropriate; by encouraging them even when they are experiencing pain; by reinforcing their courage to overcome their suffering; and most importantly, by affirming them at every opportunity.

Our guiding principles are empathy without emotionalism, compassion without pity, and love without sentimentality. Our symbol is the butterfly—a beautiful creature that starts as an ugly caterpillar that "dies," and later emerges from a "tomb" to undergo a re-creation to new life. The butterfly emerges from the cocoon through a tiny opening that presents quite a struggle for the emerging creature. But unless the butterfly is forced to go through the tiny hole, the body fluids will not be forced into its wings. The result will be that the wings will be deformed and the butterfly will never be beautiful or even fly. Our goal is to help our patients endure the loss of their "old" self, and discover a "new" and more beautiful person beneath their scars. They, like the butterfly, are forced to endure a struggle before they can feel healed. We strive to help our patients see the obstacles before them not as stumbling blocks but rather as stepping-stones.

Burn patients must first be able to trust us and have faith in our skills and dedication to them. We, as a team, had to earn that trust. Patients need to believe that we truly care about them, and that we will never abandon them. Socrates said the greatest goal in life is to "know thyself." Most of us never fully know or appreciate the person we can become. We do not fully explore our potential; our gifts and our talents or our qualities as human beings. That is human nature—to be satisfied when we are comfortable. We tend to live on the surface of our lives; the beautiful veneer of who we are, or think we are! Because our patients are so completely dehumanized, we try to help them discover the unrealized potential they may not even be aware they have. Because this requires them to expose their innermost self, we first must gain their trust and confidence. That is why it is so important for us to treat them with empathy and compassion; so that by gaining their trust, we can help them explore areas of their personhood and discover new potentials for fulfillment in spite of their suffering and scars. I like to remind them that they are unique individuals with special gifts and talents, as well as weaknesses and faults, which their Creator has given to them and to no other person. That really means that all of creation, as magnificent as it is, is incomplete without them! They have a destiny to reach.

We are skilled at helping them and their family members see each other in a new way by teaching them positive coping skills that will help re-establish a sense of complete personhood. Our goal is to help our patients emerge from their state of emptiness recognizing their potential, helping them see themselves as worthy of being happy by helping them build relationships with family and friends that are meaningful and supportive. In short, our objective is to help patients develop faith in themselves, that is, to recognize their own strength and courage and their inner beauty. We treat them as beautiful people, worthy of our respect and admiration. We affirm every little bit of progress they make. That awareness slowly and progressively rekindles in them a sense of dignity and self-esteem. Many have said, in so many words, "If you people could treat me the way you did when I was so angry with you and treated you so badly, I must be worth something!" The truth is that true beauty really does come from within. They need to buy into that truth and so believe that they have a right to be happy and lead fulfilling lives—not living in the "shadows" of life with floppy hats, long sleeves and turtlenecks.

As these events unfold, we witness a rebirth and a deepening awareness of their relationship with themselves, their families, their friends and neighbors and, their God. For many, they see God more clearly than they ever have in the past and develop a quality of relationships with others that they have never before experienced. They begin the process of discovering within themselves the power to be transformed into persons with scars who can rise above the dehumanizing effects of those scars and develop meaningful and loving relationships. Many patients tell us they experience a level of self-esteem they never enjoyed before they were burned. I could recount story after story of people who have gone through this process and who have said to me in so many words, "being burned was one of the best things that ever happened to me." Some actually celebrate a "rebirth-day" on the date they were burned. It is almost like being born again! When these results occur, we see that tragedy has turned to triumph. Patients begin seeing themselves as burn survivors instead of burn victims. What remarkable transformations we are privileged to see!

The redemptive power of suffering can lead us toward a point in our lives when we are totally empty of self and truly dependent on God. While it may be theoretically possible for persons in the state of emptiness to receive the message of God through their intellect, I believe that when we are empty, God speaks to us through our hearts! He speaks His message of hope through the witness of people willing to example His spirit. This is what I believe loving our neighbor really means. As I have seen the transformation of my patients as they experience the Burn Unit environment, I have come to believe that we can be transcendent during our life on earth. We do not need to die before we can experience a living, loving and intimate relationship with God! We are all, patients, families and staff, affirmed in a way that can not be described when we help pass the experience of being transcendent on to others. We have a covenant relationship with our patients whom we view as gifts to us, entrusted to our care. By our response, we can be gifts given to our patients by a loving God who allows us to be His instruments on earth. Life can not be any more meaningful than experiencing these gifts.

The response of family members to the efforts of the burn team in creating a supportive and peaceful environment is, perhaps, best illustrated when patients reach a state where survival is no longer possible. My older sister, Betty, preceded me in medical school by five years and was a solo practitioner in family medicine. It was she who taught me the current approach to dying patients that we currently use in the Unit. Betty Jean was an outstanding physician and was truly beloved by her many patients. In fact, at the height of her career, she would frequently have so many patients waiting to see her that her waiting room would be completely filled and patients would line up in the hallway outside her door awaiting someone to come out, knowing that there would be an empty seat. At the age of 49, she developed a breast cancer that was extremely aggressive and caused her death in less than a year. As she entered the final phase of her life, enduring radiation and chemotherapy, it became apparent that she needed too much care for my mother, who had been widowed two years previously, to provide. I suggested to Sis that she be admitted to the hospital to relieve the burdens on Mom. At that time (mid 1970s) hospice care had not yet become an option and inpatient hospitalization was the only alternative.

Before Betty agreed to be admitted, she made me promise that I would not put in a feeding tube nor would I give her IV fluids. She knew, full well, her prognosis and she, being an extremely spiritual woman, also knew that this was the end that God had called her to live out. She did not want to prolong her suffering since she was emotionally and spiritually prepared to meet God. Approximately one week after her admission it became apparent that she was requiring morphine injections every two hours to control her pain. It also became obvious that her thighs were beginning to be red and irritated from so many injections. In her semi-coma, I asked her if it would be okay to start an IV to administer IV morphine. She looked at me with startled eyes and said, "You promised." I said I would only use the IV to administer morphine so they would not have to stick her so many times.

At that time, of course, routine administration of IV morphine was unheard of and when I suggested this course of therapy to her surgeon, he objected on the grounds that he would be "killing" her. After much soul searching I wrote the order myself and found several cooperative nurses willing to administer the morphine according to my directions. I had never before done that on a patient, but it was clear to me that Sis did not want her suffering prolonged and there was no way I could help relieve her pain except by an infusion of morphine graded to meet her needs. My decision was not meant to hasten her death, but only to relieve her pain, a concept that is now accepted both ethically and morally. She died peacefully a week later and the nurses who ministered to her told me how relieved they were that they were able to participate in her relief of pain and peaceful death. The two nurses knelt at her bedside in prayer as she died. They said they "felt they were in the presence of a Saint." They thanked me for my courage in insisting on IV morphine and the privilege of caring for a great lady.

As a result of that experience I changed the way I practiced in the Burn Unit. First of all, I began to routinely use graded doses of continuous IV morphine drips to control the incredible pain endured by burn patients. I also learned that I did not have to be a "vitalist." That is, I gave up the mentality that while there was a breath of life in a patient I always had to do everything possible to save the patient. My sister, in her dying, taught me that there is a difference between prolonging life and preventing death. Too often, we physicians will not "let go" of a patient who is clearly in the process of dying and in the terminal phase of a terminal illness. We physicians, too often, insist on prolonging patients' agony in a futile attempt to "keep them alive" at all costs.

The philosophy my sister Betty taught me has remained with me and has guided my care ever since. As I look back to this experience, I recognize that even as she died she was teaching me how to be a better physician. What a marvelous gift she gave me. She continues to give her gift to many patients. Subsequent events have led to the current understanding in medicine that it is both ethical and appropriate to allow terminal patients the right to die in peace without prolonging their agony.

When any of our team members begin to question whether we are prolonging life or preventing death, they may request an ethics conference. We come together to discuss the up-to-date medical status of the patient and share our thoughts to try to form a consensus on what to recommend to the patient and/or family. If we agree that it is appropriate that aggressive therapy should be stopped, the family is invited to accept our recommendation. In this way, they are relieved of the dreadful burden of assuming "responsibility" for "causing" the death of their loved one. During these final, difficult times neither patient nor family is abandoned. Our pastoral care team and the primary care nurses remain with them throughout the final ordeal. In this kind of atmosphere, death occurs with dignity. The process affirms the surviving members of the family, eases their grief and facilitates their mourning. For the team, losing a patient after investing so much of ourselves into their care is truly painful. It is almost like losing someone in our own family. We come together to share our grief and to review the case, searching for ways to improve our standards of care in order to be sure we are giving the highest quality of care possible.

Among the most cherished gifts of affirmation we team members receive are the cards and letters from families who have lost loved ones, expressing their gratitude for the gift of healing of memories. In many cases, we receive letters and cards annually on the date their loved one died; and in several cases, contributions and gifts are sent. In one case, an annual gift has been received for the past 26 years, commemorating the death of an infant on the Burn Unit. Even in death, the *agapé* spirit can heal and relieve at least part of the pain and suffering of losing a loved one. I believe it is this kind of affirmation that gives our burn care professionals the courage to continue to work in such a stressful environment. It is one of the driving forces that helps bind us together as a community.

Another manifestation of the work of the burn team is the way we respond to children who have been abused or neglected. The T.E.A.M. is really stressed by these cases and it would be easy to become angry at the abuser. In most cases, the children are eventually returned to their parents. Our job is to be sure they will be in a safe environment. We rely on our pediatric social service counselor to define an appropriate response by uncovering the strengths and weaknesses present in the family group. It is easy to condemn the abusive person. Who could intentionally hurt a beautiful child?? We have learned however that the best thing we can do is to help the parents become good parents. In many cases, they were abused as children and they are just passing on what they were taught in their youth. Making them feel like monsters does nothing to help them change. Parenting classes, contracts for behavior and close supervision by the county child protective services are important. More than that, however, is the need to treat them in a way that encourages them to feel they are valued, in order for them to gain the self-respect and dignity they lack. It amazes me how often these abusive adults can be helped to become good and caring parents! That is the best thing we can do for their children.

Our children survivors come together at both summer and winter camps specifically designed for them. No parents, siblings or friends are permitted, only burn team members and camp counselors. They are totally free to be themselves in a protective environment of fun and opportunity. No one is whispering behind their backs, or gawking at them or asking stupid questions like, "Wow, what happened to you?" The sight of 50 to 60 children, swimming together with all their scars exposed, is awesome. The stories they share and the lives they lead are truly inspiring. No one, no matter how difficult life may be for them, can feel sorry for themselves when they see these children having fun, laughing and shouting and running and swimming together. They help each other learn how to cope with life and they come to know who are their real friends and who are not!

Our adult survivors and families meet weekly in our survivor meetings to share stories and help each other find coping skills for particular problems. They have many activities throughout the year to foster a family environment. In addition they meet annually in a spiritual retreat to help come to grips with the need for continuous growth and reaffirmation that comes with sharing their life stories. It is a privilege to watch the growth and healing taking place in so many seriously burned patients. They believe they can do anything they set their mind to doing. It is both awesome and awe inspiring!

It is at these times that the fruits of our team effort are most clearly evidenced. The joys of being part of such an endeavor not only accrue to the patients and their families but also to those of us who are part of the burn team. There is an esprit de corps among us that is palpable. Many of our burn team members have been together for over 20 years which is quite remarkable when one considers how difficult and stressful it is to work in an environment with so much pain, anxiety, fear, ugliness and stress with little or no margin for error. To be part of an environment which can help patients transcend their human condition is not only professionally quite satisfying, but moreover, the team members experience a grace which blesses their entire life and is reflected in our non-professional activities as well. The Unit is a "sanctuary" of peace and joy, yet patients may be writhing in pain, acting out their impulses by lashing out at their caregivers. We sometimes refer to this as the agony and the ecstasy of working in the Burn Unit. To paraphrase Charles Dickens in *A Tale of Two Cities*, it is the best of places to work; it is the worst of places to work. The fact that so many team members stay on the Unit for so many years attests to the fact that there must be a great deal of 'positives' working there to overcome the high personal cost of staying in such a stressful work-place. We have learned how to multiply joys and divide sorrows.

The medical student whom I described at the beginning of this chapter is now in Family Practice and, when I saw her recently, she said she still remembered her experience on the Burn Unit as one of the best rotations she had had as a student. The young man survived and has returned to his original employment. He told me that at one time, he wanted to ask me to let him die, but he was too afraid. He is, in fact, one of the patients who celebrates a rebirth-day to commemorate the anniversary of his injury. His wife shared at our last adult retreat that their marriage is much closer than it had previously been; and the family, including extended family, has been drawn together even more tightly. They both volunteer at their church and have done things they never thought they would be interested in attempting. Their lives have become richer and more rewarding and they truly thank God for His blessings. As they and the other patients shared their stories at the retreat, I sat there marveling at how God could take such tragic events and make them life giving.

One of the most gratifying aspects of what I do as an academic, relates to the interactions I have with medical students, surgical residents at various levels of training and students from other medical disciplines who rotate through the Unit and see, first hand, a different way of relating to patients and families. I have the opportunity to teach them the difference between a 'contract physician' and a 'covenant physician.' A contract mentality says "I will provide services but only that which serves my time, talent and income goals; but do not ask for anything more." By contrast, a covenant physician says, "You will be my patient and I will be your doctor. I will respond to all your needs and give you the best care I can." This is a difficult if not impossible undertaking in the present medical care system of managed care (in reality managed cost), but I want the future doctors, nurses and other health professional to know the virtue of this philosophy in the hopes they can try to orient their careers this way.

I believe that we see God most clearly when we overcome the imperfections and struggles in our lives. The greater the challenge the greater the triumph! If you were to ask me where to look for a person's soul, I would say "look for the scars for that is where you'll find their beauty," those scars on the "inside" as well as those on the "outside." God does not give us 'crosses' to punish us but rather to help us realize our depth of personhood and our ability to overcome obstacles. For it is in overcoming that which wounds us that we encounter both our inner strength and the Spirit which enables us to be transcendent.

Life, in reality, is a journey to perfect ourselves within the human limitations we have in dealing with the imperfections of our lives. The greatest force for change lies within us and is called the human spirit. It is empowered by the Creator, the Giver of Life itself, or whatever you call the Power Greater than Yourself. That power, working through our human spirit gives us the ability to overcome any obstacle, the ability to transcend our human condition. Transcendence can be defined as rising above and going beyond ordinary limits and going beyond ordinary experiences into the spiritual world of peace and joy in union with a loving and caring God. I know it is possible. I have experienced it!

Our spirit is the healing force within each of us that needs to be continually nurtured and set free so it can help us overcome our "handicaps." It is fostered when we reflect on our experiences of faith and hope, by our relationships with others who truly care for us and by those who allow us to love them. The way our spirit is nurtured is through giving and receiving unconditional love from God and from our neighbors. This love reaffirms our faith—faith in God, faith in our neighbor and faith in ourselves. The fruit of that faith is hope, the indomitable will to overcome obstacles, to use them as stepping stones rather than stumbling blocks.

The power of the human spirit is awesome. It only needs to be set free within us. That requires transcendent relationships that demonstrate the love of God for us in terms of human interactions. For most of us, real life experiences are easier to understand because they are more tangible and can be perceived in human ways. *We need to see God with skin on.* Scripture tells us that suffering is not in vain, and with God all things are possible. Jesus did not come to take away our suffering. He came to fill it with His Loving Presence.

When we respond to our suffering and the suffering of others with the supernatural gifts of faith, hope and love, we learn, ever more clearly, that God's transforming love truly gives us the grace and power to transcend our human condition. Cinders can be healed and become butterflies!

NINE

Becoming Butterflies

"When I am weakest, the Lord is strongest...for my strength
is made perfect in weakness...for when I am weak,
then am I strong." 2 Corinthians 12: 9-10

Over the years the members of the burn team have come to realize that it is not only the expertise with which each member of the burn team practices their craft, but it is the way in which it is practiced that has a profound effect on the renewal of the spirit within our patients. The symbol of our Unit is the butterfly and the symbol is prominently displayed throughout the Unit, first of all to remind the caregivers that our objective is to turn cinders into butterflies and second to help remind the patients that they are beautiful creatures of God despite their scars.

RICHARD B. FRATIANNE, M.D.

All they need to do is come to the realization that their beauty is from within.

Seriously burned patients must eventually confront the reality of their situation and it is clearly a major crisis in their life. But at that point there is the opportunity for them to see themselves differently, perhaps, than they have ever seen themselves before—that is to recognize unknown talents and gifts and potential for growth that they may never have realized they possessed.

There is no substitute for good medical care. The environment we attempt to achieve in the Burn Unit is one of nurturing patients and families by affirmation while at the same time helping them find the discipline needed to carry out their own responsibilities in the process of healing. Patients are encouraged gently, but firmly, to participate with their exercise program. Our occupational therapists outline a progressive program to teach patients the skills necessary to perform the activities of ordinary daily living. It takes a great deal of encouragement and patience. However, when patients see that they are making progress and they realize that they are responsible in part for their own progress, it is the beginning of re-establishing a sense of self-esteem in patients who have lost their dignity. It requires a firm, but gentle, coordinated effort by all the members of the burn team to gently bring patients through the rigors of their recovery with a positive attitude that makes the transcended spirit, which is already within them, come to life. Many patients have told me in so many words, "If you all could treat me the way you did, with such kindness and understanding when I was such a difficult patient, *I realized I must be worth something!*" We have witnessed the transformation of many patients whose lives were changed so dramatically through the horrible experience of their burn. I would like to tell you a few of their stories so you may believe more deeply in the transforming power of God's grace working through human beings dedicated to His service.

Bobby was a 16-year-old who lived at home where his father abused his mother and where he was beaten regularly when his father came home intoxicated. He was not doing well in school and actually was considered a real troublemaker. One evening after being beaten by his father, he took off in his family's automobile and was driving "like a crazy man" when he hit a house and the car burst into flames, seriously burning both of his legs. He sustained multiple fractures of the bones of the legs below the knees and burns from the hips down. We were faced with the inevitable decision to amputate both legs.

All the experts agreed that he should have above knee amputations on both legs. Mobility after such a bilateral procedure would have been severely limited despite modern advances in above knee prostheses. There is no good substitute for knee joints. I recognized that there was a slim chance that we could amputate below his knees, but that would require rather complicated and expensive orthopedic and plastic surgical procedures that would rotate muscles to cover exposed bone, with subsequent skin grafting. Our T.E.A.M. decision was to proceed with salvage of his knees. In actuality we replaced one simple straightforward operation with three complex and very expensive operations for each leg. I caught severe criticism from our case management department, and some of my colleagues also felt that I was wasting valuable resources. What sustained me was the knowledge that the burn T.E.A.M. had come to a consensus to save his knees. I believe that in this process, the truth of what is right is always revealed.

At the time when his surgical procedures were almost completely healed and he was nearing discharge, we were holding our annual summer camp for burned children survivors. When I made rounds that Saturday morning, Bobby had a wistful look in his eyes. He knew about the camp and he wanted to be there. Through all of his experiences on the Unit, Bobby and I had achieved a very close bond and he had come to a level of trust in others that he had never before felt. He had not yet been fitted with his prostheses, thus he was wheel chair bound. Since his parents had essentially abandoned him, there was no one I could seek for permission to bring him to camp. I signed him out in my custody, carried him to my car and brought him to camp. When I arrived I asked some of the older boys who were survivors themselves to help me with Bobby. They carried him to the lake where they had been swimming and they all swam together. Bobby with his shortened legs was able to do something he never thought he would be doing. For the next two days I had no worries because his friends looked after him like loving parents. After being sad for so long a time, it was quite a sight to see him laughing and happy, just being one of the guys.

The next year when I went to camp I was standing and talking to a friend, and I saw Bobby across a field. When he saw me, he came *running* across the field on his two prostheses and jumped into my arms. As I write this I can still feel his arms holding me tightly. Not a word was spoken. Bobby had become a model student in school, his life had been rearranged through social services and he was truly happy for the first time in a long time. He was receiving counseling and had been able to overcome his bitterness towards his family. He was planning to enroll in a chef's school after graduation from high school. The question I ask is, "What would his life have been like had he never been burned?"

Luke was 17 and getting ready to enter his senior year in high school when there was a tragic fire in his home, which took the lives of his mother and one of his three brothers. He sustained severe burns over two thirds of his body, including his face, arms and hands, trunk and thighs. At the time of his injury, Luke was an average student in high school. His father was a successful businessman who had a significant drinking problem that became unmanageable as the result of the stress associated with the events of the fire. Luke was in the hospital approximately three months with the usual kinds of complications from such a severe burn injury. He told me several times he wanted to die. We had many opportunities to discuss the need for him to see things in a positive light, that he could overcome his injuries and his scars. Life did not need to end in tragedy but could become better than it was. We developed an incredibly close bond. He told me that I was substituting for his father because his dad was so troubled that he could not always be there for him when he needed him; and he really missed his mom.

Luke confided in me, some years later, that he had had a near death experience, but after experiencing the beautiful white light and an incredible peaceful feeling, he was told to "go back," that his time had not come. He also said he kept remembering my statement; the bottle is either half full or half empty. Your choice!

He subsequently graduated from high school

and began college studies to train himself as a physical therapist. He went into practice in Florida and
began treating burn victims at the local burn center.
Several years later he asked me if I thought he had
the capacity to become a doctor. I encouraged him
and told him that the only way he would know for
sure was to "go for it" with everything he had. I
outlined for him the courses required to bring him
to the point where he would qualify for admission
to medical school. After consulting with the Dean
of Admissions at Case Western Reserve, he followed our instructions and was admitted.

Following graduation he began training in
surgery with subsequent specialization in plastic
surgery. As this is being written he has completed
his last year in training. His goal is to devote his
life to reconstructing burn victims. He is married
with three beautiful sons and lives life to the fullest
despite his burn scars. He returned to Cleveland
and helped me give a welcoming talk to the first
year medical students on the Art and Science of
Medicine. As we concluded, I asked him if he
thought he would ever have become a plastic surgeon had he not been burned. He looked intently
into my eyes, his eyes filled with tears, and he gave

me a bear hug. No words were needed. He got a standing ovation from the students!

Lucy was four when she was involved in a house fire that killed her grandmother and one of her sisters. She suffered a cardiac arrest at the scene and although given cardiopulmonary resuscitation by the firefighters who rescued her, it was 20 minutes before her little heart started to beat again. When I first saw her she had burns over 70% of her body. Her face was very badly burned. Her hands were burned so seriously that it was clear to me that she would lose *all* of the digits of both of her hands; and her feet were so critically burned that I knew they would both need to be amputated. The oxygen level in her blood was very low, to the point where there was a high probability that she had suffered severe brain damage with little chance to ever awaken.

As I looked at the devastation before me, the thought went through my mind that perhaps the most merciful thing to do to would be to let her die. Her chance of recovery was very slim; and if she survived, there was a high probability she could be severely brain damaged. If she did recover, her face would be badly scarred, her "hands" would be nonfunctional and she would have bilateral lower leg prostheses. All I had to do was be "a little slow" in responding to her critical and life threatening injuries. The nurses taking care of her had tears in their eyes as we took inventory of her devastation.

I had long since recognized that I could never quit on any child. When I asked the nurses for their opinion, they agreed we had to try. Almost against my better judgment, we set in motion a very aggressive treatment plan. Lucy required twelve surgical procedures during her initial hospitalization and months of therapy and nutritional support. She did survive. Not only did she survive, but her mind is also quite functional and she has turned out to be a very bright little girl. Her face is badly scarred, but the plastic surgeons have done remarkably well in reconstructing it so that her eyes close and her mouth opens and closes normally. Her hair has been restored to her scalp. She has no thumbs or fingers, but the plastic surgeons have given her a "grasp" in her palms. These "hands" have limited but useful function. She slips her leg prostheses on an off with remarkable ease.

Several years ago, she was admitted for reconstruction of the scars at the corners of her mouth that prevented her from opening her mouth very widely. She was having difficulty eating the little lollipops I routinely brought to her each day. As it happened she was hospitalized over the Christmas holiday. Her gift to me on Christmas morning was a giant all-day sucker. When I opened the package, I saw the glint of happiness in her eyes and she said, "I want you to have a lollipop that you can't get in your mouth either." No gift I received that Christmas was more meaningful. My grandchildren prayed for Lucy and shared the lollipop after Christmas dinner. The adults all had tears in our eyes when I told them her "story."

I have watched Lucy at summer camp the last six years. She does everything the other children do, including swimming, running and horseback riding. She participates in the tug-of-war exercises. She can run almost as fast as the other children her age despite wearing prostheses. She has turned out to be very bright and uses a computer with ease. She is in the normal grade for her age at a special school for the handicapped. Not only is she a remarkable person, but anyone who sees her can not help but also be inspired by her courage. Who could feel sorry for oneself in her presence?

Sometimes when I watch her, so full of life, I think back to the first time I saw her and thank God for helping me decide not to deny her a chance at a full and happy life.

Rick was 22 years old when he was involved in a house fire in which he received serious burns over 80 per cent of his body. Rick had been a strikingly handsome young man and the object of affection for many young ladies. He had finished high school, but was unemployed at the time of his injury. He spent three months in the Burn Unit and had six surgical procedures that resulted in restoration of his ability to function, but which left him with serious cosmetic deficits.

He became quite bitter and withdrawn. He had no family and none of his friends visited. He was basically alone during the ordeal of his recovery. As much as other members of the burn team and I tried to develop a relationship with him, Rick had a way of shutting off any conversation that required him to expose his true feelings. He built a wall around himself and would not let any of us in and, of course, kept himself trapped in his forlorn, brooding and self-destructive "prison."

Rick was readmitted three months later for a

reconstructive procedure on his hand. I remember it was a Sunday morning and I was making rounds in the hopes of getting to my parish in time to serve as a Eucharistic Minister at the 11:30 Mass. As I entered his room, Rick, for some reason, seemed anxious to talk. I sat with him and he started to pour out his heart. He was very angry that none of his friends came to visit because they all thought he was ugly. He sounded as though he was thinking about doing himself harm when he was released, after this surgical procedure. I realized that this was a crisis point in his life. I told him that even though all of his friends had abandoned him, the members of the burn team had not abandoned him and I would never abandon him. He recognized that I had visited him daily and that I was concerned for his welfare. Moreover, I told him that God loved him. He said, "Dr. Frat, you can't possibly know that because you do not know what I have done in my life." He then proceeded to tell me a rather sordid tale that culminated in the fact that he had been paid to set the fire that had caused his own destruction.

As I listened to his story I realized that he had finally come to trust me enough to divulge the secrets which had haunted him throughout his hospitalization and which he had been afraid to express. When I told him that God loved him, his first response was to pour out his story in anger and he concluded by saying, "See, there is no way that God could love me now." I looked intently into his eyes and held his hands in mine and I told him, "I am *sure* God loves you." He responded, "How can you be sure?" I said, "I *know* He loves you because I love you and I could not love you unless He loved you *first*." The tears began to stream down his face and his hands began to tremble. Needless to say, I did not make it to 11:30 Mass that day, but I believe we experienced The Eucharist together, which is to say, God's Living Presence within us.

From that day forward, Rick has been a changed man. He has found faith in God, he has become gainfully employed and, although he has not married, he has enjoyed a meaningful social life. Several years later he came to visit me and brought me a gift. Before I opened the box I told him he was the only gift I needed. And he said, "No, you have to open it." It contained a beautiful rosewood framed silver crucifix under a crystal cover. On the back it said, "Thank you for helping me find God."

As I look back on that awesome experience I recognize that there truly is a transformation when a person feels the Presence of God within him. The discovery of that truth is, I believe, unparalleled in human existence.

Kate was a beautiful 22 year old aspiring actress who was a regular performer in summer stock productions. She surely was on her way to stardom. In the play she was rehearsing, she played the part of a nun who was injured in a fire and whose faith was shaken as a result. As fate would have it, while driving home from a rehearsal, she was involved in an accident with a tanker truck which exploded and consumed her car in flames.

Kate sustained a massive, life threatening burn of 65% of her body, involving face, hands, arms and legs—all the visible parts of her body. Kate endured many surgeries including our best efforts in giving her good function and cosmetics. When we told her the scars were permanent, she believed her acting career had ended. She went through the stages of denial, anger and bargaining, but had great difficulty accepting this terrible interruption of her dreams of a stage career.

The nurses taking care of Kate were her peers.

In many ways they identified with her broken heart and responded with extraordinary empathy and compassion. We kept telling her that she could still do whatever she wished in life, and not quit on herself. The team reminded her that she had a great inner beauty, which is what helped make her the actress she was in the process of becoming. It was that beauty which radiated out of her when she was on stage.

Following discharge from the Burn Unit, Kate courageously went through a year of intense physical and occupational therapy and slowly came to accept her scars. She had reached the level of acceptance that the reality of her burns were permanent but not dehumanizing. We were overjoyed when she told us she was planing to try to resume her acting career.

The following summer, Mary and I received an invitation to "Opening Night" at a local summer stock production...Staring Kate! There she was, on stage, radiant in her acting ability, wearing her support garments on her legs and one hand. I had a difficult time seeing the production because my eyes were misty most of the evening. Imagine the courage it took for her to do that. Imagine the positive self image she had regained. Imagine the transformation of spirit she had undergone with the help of her family, friends and caregivers. At the reception following the play, Kate introduced us to her fiancé. His love for Kate was clearly visible. He had such pride in her accomplishments. As we drove home that evening, Mary and I shared our admiration for Kate and our recognition that beauty is present in the spirit of everyone and that sometimes people have to go through terrible difficulties to discover their true potential. It is a revelation of the power of the human spirit when survivors like Kate witness that truth to the world. She had overcome her brokenness and had become transcendent.

In my 30 years as director of the Burn Center, there have been literally thousands of such stories. I have included only these few so that you may believe in God's transforming grace that can help individuals who suffer such tragedies to live lives of great beauty and fulfillment. In many cases, I am convinced that the lives they lead are more beautiful, more fulfilling, more profoundly filled with the richness of human experience than they are likely to have led had they not suffered their burns.

These stories demonstrate, unmistakably, the power of the Spirit working through a community dedicated to healing those with incurable problems and incredible tragedies. There is no "magic." There are no bolts of lightning that flash down from heaven, there are no sudden re-creations that happen. There are, however, tiny, repeated miracles in the transformation of the human spirit, which fill the lives of patients, families and caregivers with a sense of peace and joy beyond all understanding. That power constantly re-energizes the members of our burn team to continue to try to practice life-giving relationships with those entrusted to our care.

My "Passover"

*"Though I walk through the valley of darkness, I shall fear
no evil for You are my rod and my staff." Psalm 23*

In late summer of 1999, my life was running at
its usual complex and hectic pace. The Burn
Unit was exceedingly busy with many critical
patients requiring very close supervision. We had
a very high load of ambulatory patients to be seen
each week in the clinic and I was preparing for a
number of national presentations. Mary and I had
just returned from France where I had delivered
a scientific paper on advanced burn care and life
was quite wonderful, yet stressful. I became
aware that I was becoming exceedingly tired,
more so than usual. I had a slight but persistent
headache over the right side of the top of my

head. Several people noted later that I was walking favoring my left foot and I was not sure my left hand was functioning normally.

After an exceedingly stressful day, which began early in the morning with the admission of a patient with 80% body burn and ending with a very large ambulatory clinic, I felt I was about to lose consciousness and asked for help. Fortunately I was making evening rounds on the Burn Unit and the nurses and resident doctors came to my assistance immediately. I am told I suffered a grand mal seizure. I have no memory from that point until the afternoon of the following day when my neurosurgeon, a wonderful man who had been an intern on my general surgical and Burn Unit service many years before, came to tell me some dreadful news. I had a lesion approximately the size of a golf ball in the right side of my brain. He told me that there was a 90-95% chance that this was a rapidly growing malignant tumor and that he had scheduled me for major surgery the following Monday. Wow!

When he left, my mind went back approximately 15 years to the night before Mary was facing surgery for a lump in her breast. I remember she was sitting in my lap. We prayed together and talked about all the wonderful things that we had experienced since we met. We recognized that whatever her lump was, it already was. She had had many lumps removed in the past, and they were all benign. If it was cancerous, we asked God for the strength to bear what had to be borne as a result of all that would happen. We both received a great deal of consolation and strength from our mutual prayer as we sat holding each other tightly. There were tears, but we did not waver in our faith that God would see us through whatever we faced.

Mary survived radical surgery for her breast cancer and, by the grace of God, has remained cancer free these past 18 years. Although the experience was both a great emotional and physical stress for her, she has borne the challenge with grace and strength inspired by her faith and by the support of her family and friends. Remembering her ability to accept with grace, that which could not be changed, I was filled with hope and renewed in my faith as I faced my own ordeal. I knew Mary would understand exactly what I was going through and by her experience, be with me in a very special way helping me through all my doubts and fears. It was just one more gift of love Mary was able to give me at a critical period of my life!

The neurosurgeon asked me, "How aggressive do you want me to be tomorrow? How radical do you want me to be?" I knew exactly what he meant. Part of the difficulty of being a patient when you are a doctor is that you know too much. I told him that I wanted him to "go after it" wherever it takes you because that is the only chance I would really have for long-term survival, even though that was unlikely. Knowing where the lesion was, I knew that if he did radical surgery, there would be a strong likelihood that I would awaken at least partially blind and paralyzed on my left side.

In reality there was no place to hide; there was no way to defer a decision. There was no way to ask for another test that might indicate that it really was not a cancer. No, it had to be faced and it had to be faced then. There was no alternative. Could the surgeon remove it all? What function would I have left after surgery? How long would I survive? How much pain would I have to endure? Despite all these fears, I told him to be radical!

When I saw Mary she had already been told of the diagnosis and prognosis. The children were on their way in from various parts of the country to be with me the weekend before my surgery. I felt a great sense of consolation knowing that I would see my family and all the grandchildren. This was particularly important to me because if I were to be blind, I wanted to be able to imprint one last time, their faces in my memory so I would never forget how they looked. I also was very happy to have my brother Doug, his wife Carol and my sister Mary Joy coming to be with us so they too would also be firmly etched in my memory bank.

The Sunday before surgery was a glorious day with the grandchildren crawling over me on my bed, hugging and kissing and holding on. I was thinking how much I had hoped to watch them grow and perhaps graduate from high school and start college. My oldest granddaughter, Melissa, a high school senior, seemed to be exceedingly mature and grown up. I was so proud of her. I remember feeling so gifted from God to have so many blessings given to me and I thanked Him for each of my wonderful children and grandchildren; and recognized once again that the bedrock of my life upon which all of this had rested was Mary.

That day, Scott my elder son, opened the Bible

and began reading from the New Testament. My family frequently finds great strength in opening the Scripture randomly and reading a passage. We have found that somehow or other the passages we read frequently have direct bearing on the situations we are encountering in our lives. That Sunday was no different. He kept reading passages that somehow seemed to be specifically directed to giving all of us strength and wisdom and courage. Each seemed to center on God's abiding love for us, and the sharing that followed the Scripture reading involved everyone and was consoling to each of us. It was a time of great peace in the midst of what could have been great turmoil. How wonderful is the gift of faith.

As visiting hours slowly drew to a close, the family started to leave. When Mary left, my room became empty. I realized I was alone in the semi-darkness. My thoughts turned to my family's words of encouragement, and the hugs and kisses of support. My brother, Doug, and Carol, my sister by marriage, encouraged me to keep the faith and work hard to recover. Carol held me very tightly and told me she loved me and to be strong. Sometimes I get the feeling that she does not believe I know that she loves me, but I *do* know, and I value her love very much. She is such a wonderful and gentle lady, who has done so much with her life. It is a privilege for me to have her as part of my family. And my brother, Doug, as he was leaving, bent over and kissed me and told me he loved me, and I do not *ever* remember him doing that before. I am sure he has. It made me feel *so* good. Reflecting back, I think we were never able to develop the depth of relationship that we could have. Part of the problem was because we did not live close together. We did not see much of each other for long periods of time. As I look back, that is one of the things that I wish were different, and I hope to make that a priority, as the future unfolds. Somehow, some way, I must do that.

I remember getting a phone call from Anita, my sister in North Andover, Massachusetts. I could hear the trembling in her voice, as she tried to console me, and I could sense the depth of her caring and love for me over the phone. She is a terrific person. I remember Scott, my oldest son, telling me he really loved me and was proud to be my son. I remember Kay, my daughter by marriage, telling me how much she loved and respected me and how she hoped that Bryan, their son, would grow up to be like me. I remember Melissa kissing me and telling me that, as soon as she could drive, we were going to spend a Saturday afternoon having lunch and an ice cream soda and going to a movie—something we two had done together many times when she was a little girl. I felt good, hearing that.

I remember my son Greg and his wife Linda, my daughter by marriage, holding me and trembling, and reminding me that God would be with me. They are very spirit-filled and lead exemplary Christian lives. Their four children have a marvelous window, their parents, through which to see God's grace. I remember Susan, my middle daughter, telling me that she had had a long conversation with the Lord, Who told her everything would be all right. Of course, neither of us knew what "all right" meant, but as I lay there, alone in the darkness, her words confirmed in my mind that God was promising not to abandon me. That gave me a great sense of courage and peace. My youngest daughter Lisa, a professional hairdresser, cut my hair during the afternoon and I remembered the hair, mixed with tears, falling on the sheet covering my shoulders. She held me tightly as she was about to leave, telling me how proud she was to have me as her father; and David, her husband and my son by marriage, saying, "I love you, Dad." They provide a wonderful environment of love for their three children.

What a great sense of strength I received from my children. I remembered the look on the little grandchildren's faces, as they entered the room. I saw fear and anxiety in their eyes. They did not know why, but they knew something was very serious, and as they climbed on my bed, to kiss me and hug me and tell me they loved me, I worried that they might have to pay a terrible price, if I could not recognize them after surgery. I remembered Mary, my "rock" holding me tightly and looking deep into my eyes—no blinking, no tears, but communication from soul to soul, as she reminded me that we had gone through many tough times and always came through "on top." We would do this together, again. She was the last to leave, and I had the image of her face with me that night. When she had gone, my first thought was to try holding back the dawn from coming. Life was likely to change dramatically with the coming of the morning. I had to get myself ready.

As I lay in the darkness alone with my thoughts,

I began a journey as my life passed before me. I thought of all the patients I had treated who overcame unbelievable odds to make a life after devastating injuries and burns. The transcendence of their lives gave me great courage to believe I could overcome what was likely to be a true test of what I believed. It was a form of prayerful review of all that had brought me to this moment in time, especially the decision Mary and I made to be 'medical missionaries' in Cleveland and all that has meant in our lives.

It was a most profound experience of the living Jesus I had ever experienced. I offered myself completely to God. I offered Him everything I had tried to do in His name throughout my life. I came before Him totally empty, totally vulnerable but somehow strangely at peace. I asked Him, first, that He would be with me wherever this journey took me. Of course, I already knew the answer because we had been through many, perhaps less poignant moments together, but He had never failed to be with me. So I was asking Him for something I was confident He was already going to grant me. In my weakness, I began to ask God for favors—first, that my children would be inspired to assume, in a loving way, the responsibility to care for their mother, if I could not. And, second, I told Him that I could bear the loss of my sight and my motor function, but that He please help me retain my memory. As precious as sight is, at that moment I was ready to give it away, in order not to lose my memory of my family, my friends and the courageous burn survivors, because they are the people who have made me who I am. Without them I would have nothing to give. At that moment in my life, I really knew that love is stronger than anything and the love of my family and friends would sustain me, no matter what.

I recited the XXIII Psalm. I put myself totally in His hands and said, "Thy will be done." At that moment I found myself with Jesus in the Garden of Gethsemani, and for a brief, but overpowering moment, I was suddenly aware that *I knew* how He felt when He faced His ordeal. It was electrifying. He let me feel His pain for an instant so that my pain would be diminished; He would carry it for me! The tears came—tears of joy. Through my tears, all I kept repeating was, "Thank You, Lord, for such a great gift. Truly Thou are great and good and all creation rightly gives You thanks and praise." I was overcome with an incredible feeling of peace and I began reciting the Lord's Prayer. At some point during the prayer I went to sleep and slept soundly and peacefully until I was awakened early in the morning. When I awoke I still had that incredible feeling of peace even though I knew what was about to happen. The most amazing thing was that I was no longer afraid. At five o'clock, my nurse, Mike, came in to give me my medications in preparation for surgery. He spoke to me very gently, and called me his buddy. He told me that he would be with me until the transporters took me down to the operating room.

He put his arm on my shoulder and sat on the edge of the bed for what seemed like an hour. As we talked and shared, I told him what I had experienced that evening and during the night, and I told him the only thing that kept me from being totally at peace was the fact that my eldest daughter was unable to be with me on Sunday. He tried to fill that pain as best he could, by reassuring me that she must love me, and that something very serious prevented her from coming to be with me. And then he told me he had not talked to his father for more than two years. I asked him—I pleaded with him—"Please do not let that happen, whatever the reason, *whatever* the reason, find a way to get together. Do not let it happen." I admitted I did not know the circumstances, but since he did, he was the one that could find a way. The last thing I remember him saying before they wheeled me to the operating room was that he would try to reconcile himself with his father. I felt good. I thought how wonderful it is that God is always at work, bringing people to the fold, regardless of the circumstances. Months later, he told me he had reconciled with his father and both were very happy to be reunited. The Hound of Heaven never sleeps.

In the hallway to the operating room I met Mary, my son Scott and my daughter Lisa. I could see the pain in their faces and the strength they were trying to give me when they held me and kissed me. And then I turned to Mary. Even though it was a little after 6:00 in the morning, she looked beautiful, in fact radiant. I held her face in my hands so I could look deeply into her eyes. I told her that if I were to be blind, I wanted her image to be the last thing I saw, so it would be on my mind forever. There were no tears. No words were spoken. The communication between us was profound. The softness of her kiss was all I remembered until I awoke from surgery.

The next thing I recall, I think I was sitting up on the operating room table. My first thought was, "Why haven't they started the surgery yet?" I could see perfectly and I was not paralyzed or weak on my left side. I thought there had been a problem; perhaps the surgery had not yet begun; I had a complication or it had to be postponed. I suddenly realized that my anesthesiologist was shouting in my right ear, "It's only an abscess, Frat; it's not a tumor; it's only an abscess." I did not have cancer! How could that be? With God, all things are possible!

As the impact of those words settled over me I fell asleep and did not awaken for a number of hours. I was later to learn that the doctors in the operating room were singing and dancing when the diagnosis was established. All the doctors I had asked to be my caregivers were chosen because, in addition to being experts, they were men of great faith, Jewish, Christian and Moslem, who lived their spirituality openly. In addition, each was highly respected in his field. I regret that I was unable to appreciate all that happened in the operating room, but what happened does not surprise me because of who they are.

During the four hours I was in the operating room, I came to understand that the T.E.A.M. in the Burn Unit had provided a special place for my family, including the grandchildren, to wait comfortably. In addition they had provided food and beverage for breakfast and lunch in a private area where my family could be together in their thoughts and prayers. When I was told about this, I recognized that my extended family was there for my immediate family. They had all waited in anxious expectation, even though the members of the burn team had to carry on with their awesome responsibilities of caring for both inpatients and outpatients that morning. But it was done with such sensitivity that my family received tremendous support during those trying hours. Needless to say, the rejoicing that went on when the news was finally brought to them was truly a manifestation of the depth of their love and concern for me by everyone, my extended and immediate family.

When I awoke, there were lots of tears and hugs. I remember my cheeks were wet from the tears of those who were kissing me. All I could do was thank God in a special way for His Providence. It was the end of the most remarkable night I have ever lived, with God's wonderful mercy and grace, spoken to me by my family and friends, who truly are His image and likeness to me. I realized my good fortune to have such a beautiful family and such wonderful friends. I felt the glow of His Presence within me. In a way I felt unworthy of the wonderful blessings I had been given. How could anyone feel worthy of such a magnificent manifestation of love—the love of God made real by the love of family and friends. Truly, the greatest 'prize' in life!

After four days in the Surgical Intensive Care Unit, I was transferred to the special Brain Injury Rehabilitation Unit that is part of the Trauma Center at our county hospital. There I was to meet another very dedicated team of professionals who began the task of putting the functions of my brain back together. This involved cognitive, occupational, physical, music and art therapy. Each modality had its special purpose and result. What was amazing to me is how well coordinated and integrated each of these team members performed. Only then did I realize how sick I was at the time of my surgery. I had lost my balance and coordination. I had lost spatial orientation and the ability to process complex problems. Clearly, there was a great deal I needed to regain before I could resume my life as it was before surgery. My therapists and my nurses became very special to me and were included with the greater body of supporters I had in my prayers of thanksgiving to my God.

Another large part of my recovery was due to the overwhelming outpouring of love and prayers that I received from innumerable people, some of whom did not even know me, but who had heard about my condition through a newspaper article. It was a glorious manifestation of the Mystical Body of Jesus alive in the world—the true definition of the Church. There was no way I could separate the love, the prayers and the good wishes I received from so many people who cared deeply for me from the extraordinary prayer experience I had the night before surgery. I believe, very strongly, that it was in fact *because* of the prayers and sacrifices that were being offered on my behalf that I had the courage to face God and empty myself to His will. If nothing else, this experience has demonstrated to me in a most vivid way what the concept of 'Church' really means; the Mystical Body of Christ formed into a community of believers, centered on the Christian axis of unconditional love. The power of a Christian Community *in action* is awesome.

I remember my sister, Mary Joy, coming to see me in the evening three days after surgery. She performed a Reiki service of healing. This was something that was totally unfamiliar to me. It was a wonderful experience of peace and joy, with the most unusual manifestations of color and images in my head. I can't explain the experience except to say there was this constant, beautiful soft white glow. It was not *just beautiful*. It was *dynamic*. It was like melted marshmallows swirling in all directions. It helped me feel peaceful and calm. My sister left quietly thinking I was asleep. Even after I realized she had gone, these sensations stayed with me until I fell asleep. Was I dreaming? I'm not sure. I've never experienced anything like that before or since then.

When I awakened the next morning, I realized I had slept very soundly for the first time since surgery. I was no longer exhausted. I do not know what Sis did or how she did it—all I know is that her prayer was extremely powerful, and it came through to me in a most wonderful way. Even though I would need two months to complete my recovery, I knew that morning, that things would be fine eventually. My prayers and my family's prayers had been answered beyond any of our expectations. The Angel of death had passed over me. Thanks be to God. My "Passover" was complete. I was transformed into a butterfly.

Saving Power

"Do this in remembrance of Me." Luke 22: 19

Perhaps, the Scripture passage in which I most want to participate is John 15, the discourse of the Last Supper. The one person I do not wish to be is Judas Iscariot, but he has already absented before the profound events that unfold in the breaking of the bread. As my life has grown richer and more meaningful through the experiences of being willing to live *agapé* relationships with others, I have come to recognize that being willing to sacrifice myself for the sake of others, which is a required part of unconditional love, is the principle mechanism by which I am drawn ever more tightly to a more intimate relationship with God; and Jesus truly becomes my brother.

As we read the beautiful words of John 15, we know how it all turns out since we read those words in context of what we know happened. And so the discourse for me is, in reality, a prayer from Jesus to the Father through His apostles. He wants to fortify them and give them the mechanisms, the strength, the means to be able to live loving relationships so vividly in the world that His message will be carried on to future generations. The person I most frequently find myself being in this passage is Philip. Jesus reviews His entire life in grace and recounts the examples of His love as He has lived it with His friends and followers. And His message is crystal clear, "Love one another as I have loved you. As I am in the Father and the Father is in Me, so I am in you that you may be in Me. I am the Vine and you are the branches, and if you live the *agapé* love that I have witnessed to you, you will bear much fruit because those you love, unconditionally, will come to know the Father more deeply." He reminds them that sacrificial love is from the Father, and every time it is lived in the world the Father is made known. After all of this explanation and sharing from the deepest part of His heart, Philip asks Him, "but we do not know the Father; show us the Father."

Many times when I am feeling lost or over-whelmed, I catch myself saying in so many words, "Jesus, show us the Father. I am lost." And I must remind myself, hopefully, of His words, "When you see Me, you see the Father" because God *is* Love and the personification of that love is Jesus Himself. Jesus' presence in the world *is* the presence of the Father in the world and His Holy Spirit continues to live in the world in the minds and hearts of those individuals who live loving relationships, first with the Father and then with their neighbors. If Christians are the Mystical Body of Christ, then we must be the living presence of the Father in the world. I believe that when Jesus consecrated the bread and the wine ending with the phrase, "Do *this* in memory of me," He was not just telling us to continue the tradition of *saying* these words. Do *this* also meant, "Continue to live the life in grace that I have shown you by My life." When we live the life in grace, Jesus becomes real, truly real, flesh and blood real, in the world.

I have come to believe that when I receive Holy Communion, I truly receive His living presence. One piece of bread on the paten represents my life in grace, my gifts to Him since my last Eucharist; and a drop of water mixed with the wine in the chalice represents my sacrifice for others, my *agapé* relationships that I have tried to live. That is what I am offering to Him. Oh, I certainly carry a lot of baggage (sins) and my offering is not very great, but it is *not nothing*. Everyone who is attending Mass with me has put in their small piece of bread and their drop of wine as their gift to God as well. Together, we make a considerable offering to God! The absolute tragedy of our religion is that we do not explain, well enough, to worshippers that *their* offering is not just a piece of bread, but it is *their life in grace that is offered to God, through the priest on the altar*. The gifts of our collective lives in grace, imperfect as they are, are offered to the Father. God then adds the Perfect Life in Grace of Jesus to our gifts and His Presence on the altar is *Real*. Of course, when the priests elevate the Host for us to see, It has already been broken, although they frequently hold the pieces so It looks whole. We must always keep in mind that Jesus comes to us "broken," that is, He comes to us having made

Himself vulnerable to our rejection of His saving message. If we are to be His loving presence in the world, we too must be "broken," that is, to be vulnerable to those we profess to love unconditionally! Perhaps that is a frightening thought, but worthy of our consideration.

Unfortunately, too few Christians realize that they really do live a life in grace. They do not realize that, in fact, they do live *agapé* relationships. They may just be unaware of what "life in grace" means. Most everyone tries to live a good life, following the Ten Commandments and trying to love each other as best they can. We are all sinners but we are all the Lord has to entrust with the opportunity to carry on the tradition of *"doing this."* I have thought long and hard, "Why do we not tell the people it is their life in grace which is essential to bringing Jesus to life on the altar and thereby into the world! As I sit in church and watch a young mother with three small children, using Mary, my wife, as an example, I think to myself, this mom obviously has gotten up in the middle of the night many times to nurture her children when they are sick. Then she gets up in the morning to dress them, pack their lunches and get them off to school. Later she picks them up and drives them to soccer practice and ballet practice and baseball practice and all the things that are part of a young family's activities. Somehow she finds time to get to the store and cook supper and get her children off to bed and then maybe finds some time to relax and spend some quality time with her husband. Maybe she will get some sleep. My goodness, this woman lives *agapé* relationships throughout the day, day after day, sacrificing herself for her family in an unsung, often unrecognized way. She, unfortunately, most likely may not even realize that it is the magnificent life of grace she lives that brings Jesus to life on the altar and in her home.

A father who works hard to provide for his family's security, and may take a second job in order to guarantee that he will have enough money to send his children to college, is an example of sacrificial love. A man who willingly gives up his free time to look after things about the house, to make sure that his family is safe and secure also witnesses to that love. A person who goes about his life day in and day out, sacrificing himself for his wife and children, may never realize that his life is a wonder-filled reflection of unconditional love. Of course, they, like all of us, do things imperfectly; but God forgives us the 99 things we do wrong and glorifies us with His Living Presence for those things that we do in His name, as we try our best to live His life in the world. While we need to come before God with contrition for our weakness, we must do it with dignity for He has chosen us to do our part of fulfilling the mission in life He has given us.

I truly believe that Jesus can not be real for us, in our Eucharistic Celebration, unless it is by the offering of our life in grace we make to Him. That, I believe, is why there must be two or more present to have a valid Eucharistic Celebration. We need to offer our gifts together to make them a worthy offering. He said, "Where two or more are gathered in My name, there I am in their midst." God is alive in the world through His Holy Spirit Who dwells in each of us. There is no other way to explain how Jesus can truly be alive in the world, except that we have to be His eyes and ears, His hands, His feet, His heart, His will, His faith, His hope and His love. When we gather together in faith to share our spiritual lives, He comes to life in our celebration in a way that would be impossible without our participation. Truly alive!

I keep praying that one day all people will come to understand, more fully, that they are an essential and a magnificent part of the Eucharistic Celebration. Those who feel that the Sacrifice of the Mass merely relives Jesus' death, fail to realize a basic truth of our faith. His sacrificial love asks us not to die for Him, all at once as He did, but to live for Him, giving away our lives 'inch by inch and day by day' in the little sacrifices we make, called unconditional love. I believe that if all Christians were of this same mind, we would not have the splintering of the Christian faith over terms like 'transubstantiation' and 'living presence.' It is clear, at least to me, that if our life in grace is real and we offer that to God in our celebration, then God is real in the presence of His Son, Jesus. And the bread and wine truly are His body and blood which nourish us in order for us to continue to try to live loving relationships in a world that is hostile to God's teachings. Those of us who try to bring Jesus to life in the world through our relationships with others in the environments in which we live, must constantly be strengthened through our prayer and study and our reception of the living presence of God in the Eucharist. Otherwise we almost certainly will be overwhelmed by the hostility in the world which is so reflective of selfish, self-centered relationships, in its many permutations.

I have come to believe that *Jesus and I make an overwhelming majority* in any environment in which I find myself. When my life gets frazzled and the pressures mount, I find myself struggling to continue to live loving relationships with my family, friends and patients. At those times I fall back on the knowledge that He is in me and His strength can be my strength, if only I acknowledge it and accept it. As long as I recognize that He is the leader and I keep myself from doing things my way, I believe we can overcome any problem we face. I just have to learn to react to others as He would respond. When I might face these circumstances, I just ask myself, "What would Jesus do?"

One example to illustrate how much I try to rely on this thought is when I must give bad news to families whose loved ones are dying. How would Jesus tell them?? I know they are completely "at my mercy" literally. If I tell them insensitively, I can wound them deeply. I visualize holding their hearts in my hands, knowing if I treat them gruffly, I can really hurt them. They must go on living and the hope is, by my interactions, based upon the patient/physician relationship I have already established with them, they will feel my compassion and accept that which can not be changed, with grace. Moreover, that grace they experience may bring them into a closer relationship with each other and with their God, whatever their faith may be! I have seen this attitude work 'miracles.'

I have struggled for a long time, trying to understand the first of The Beatitudes, "Blessed are the poor in spirit for the kingdom of God is theirs." First of all, it would seem that we should be rich in spirit, to be filled with His holy presence. I have now come to understand that in order to be poor in spirit, a spirit-filled person must give "it" away. Of course, the more we give away, the more we receive and the more we have to give away! The other thing I have learned is that the first Beatitude (be-attitude) says the kingdom *is* theirs, not *shall be* as in the other Beatitudes. That is, we can have a living, loving and personal relationship with God in this, our human life! We do not have to be dead in order to be with God. We have been given the power to be transcendent! And, by giving away our love for God we can help others see the beauty of a personal relationship with their God in their life, a life filled more abundantly with the transcendent spirit alive in them. It is and always has been my primary motivation in my work in the Burn Unit once I came to understand. I have seen "cinders" become "butterflies." This is without question, the greatest gift we can give to one another.

I am learning, ever more deeply, that the Hound of Heaven never rests. My spiritual journey has brought me through the dark valley and just as He promised, Jesus was with me every step of the way. He bore me up. It is in fact the last chapter of my spiritual journey that has been the impetus for me to put my thoughts into words in this book. I have been so filled with the presence of the Holy Spirit through these events I can not keep my joy inside. I am compelled to share it with you, the readers, who might find the message expressed in this book as a way of seeing more clearly and feeling more deeply the presence of the Holy Spirit within your lives.

I did not choose Him. He chose me first. He has invited me on a glorious journey, lived in His love.

RICHARD B. FRATIANNE, M.D.

I have witnessed the transformation of so many lives from the depths of fear, anxiety, ugliness and pain into individuals whose beauty shines forth so brilliantly that the imperfections and "scars" disappear and the love of God is manifest through them. There is an example in my life that illustrates this truth in a beautiful way. Some years ago, Mary and I purchased a bowl carved from iron wood. As you may know, iron wood has many deep cracks that run along the grain of the wood. The artist, in this case, filled these crevices by inlaying turquoise in a silver base. The resulting beauty is spectacular with the dark wood grain contrasting with the blue of the stones inlaid with silver. In essence, the artist took the imperfections of the wood and made them the most beautiful part of his artwork. That is what God does for us. He fills in what is lacking in our humanness with His gifts of love and forgiveness which transforms each of us into beautiful, more perfect signs of His creation. By His grace, we become butterflies! When I look for God, I do not lift my eyes up to the sky; rather this is what I do. Try it. Look into the eyes of those who love you and allow you to love them. Look into the eyes of someone who is suffering physical or emotional pain.

Look into the eyes of the poor, the dying and those who have lost hope. Look into the eyes of a happy child or a family, laughing and joyful in each other's company. *There* you will see God. If you can not see God in your neighbors, you will not see Him anywhere. His Spirit is in each one of us if we but have eyes to see Him! What will be reflected back to you is the absolute certainty that *God is alive in you!*

And finally, have the courage and humility to look into a mirror; not just any mirror but one that reflects 100% of the light, so you can see all your blessings, your unique gifts and talents and potential, and all your blemishes and weaknesses. Look for the real you; come face to face with all that you are. We are told we are created "in His Image and Likeness." I believe it is the other way around. We have been created to image (reflect) His Likeness. Let me repeat that statement … We have been created to *Image His Likeness!* If you are troubled by past indiscretions (sins) and feel unworthy, remember that *the one among us who has sinned the most knows the power of God's forgiveness the best.* Look intently whether you are a saint or a sinner … His forgiving spirit *will* be there. Have courage! … Look intently! … You will see God reflected back, always … calling us to be more complete in our dignity, our self-esteem and our happiness. I have come to believe that it is His Presence, alive in every one of us, which is the source and the secret of our spiritual journeys. *His Spirit, alive in us, is the most powerful force in all creation!*

I know I have been the recipient of so much love that it is impossible to recount. Be assured that prayer does work. As I enter the next phase of my life, I am spending a great deal of time in prayer—first, to thank Him for the "un" believable blessings He has given me; second, to begin to discern what it is that He is asking from me in the future. At one point in my life I felt that I was unworthy of all that I had received from Him. I realize now that by sharing the gifts and talents He has given me, I have in some small way helped Him come to life in the world, in my own unique and often flawed way. That, of course, should be the goal of every Christian, that is, to try to live their life in such a way that others know God better.

The revelation I received to orient my secular life to serve God as a surgeon has resulted in helping people, some of whom were horribly burned, realize, somehow, that they have the power within themselves to live transcendent lives of incredible beauty, filled with dignity and self-esteem. I have seen many cinders transformed into butterflies. What has happened, unexpectedly, is that in my personal journey to help heal others who are suffering and in need of affirmation and compassion, I myself have been transformed from a cinder into a butterfly in the process.

Once again, I am reassured that what we give away freely in love is always returned to us seven times seventy fold! Of course, the greatest lesson that can be learned from these experiences is that everyone can choose to live life in such a way that they help others become butterflies. By helping others become healed, each one of us can become a beautiful butterfly and live a life of peace and joy beyond all understanding. The journey continues and the end has not yet been revealed. The courage and strength I receive from those who love me clearly shows me the depth of God's love for me and gives me the courage and the will to try to continue to live out His plan is for me.

As I prepare for retirement, I have received a beautiful message from God, delivered through my sister Mary Joy during a moment when she was in deep reflection and prayer. "When anyone retires from any part of their work, into which they have put their mind, heart and soul, there inevitably arises a feeling of grief, that all they have put into place will be systematically undone by those who may follow in that work. This is the time to release all things IN FAITH. In that way, everything will work for the glory of God because it now becomes God's work to use what I have done in ways never to be known by me, even until the end of time." This message says to me that He is asking me to surrender my control and rest confidently in God; experiencing the joy of knowing I have given all, to the best of my ability, to the One I have tried to serve. My prayer is to remain open to His words of wisdom and consolation.

Each of our journeys is sacred. We live our individual journey in the hope of experiencing God's redeeming unconditional love so that by experiencing this love, we may pass it on to those who follow after us. That is the responsibility God gives, and we accept when we call ourselves Christians and choose to follow Him. He gives us the privilege of passing on "the Keys to the Kingdom" to our loved ones, our children, our grandchildren, our friends and even our enemies if we can. Each of us can try to turn cinders into butterflies.

The circle of God's love is unbroken. It is just passed on and on and on and on. Jesus said the kingdom of heaven is within you!

HEAVEN is not a destination. IT is the journey.

Glory be to the Father, and to the Son and to the Holy Spirit; as it was in the beginning, is now and ever shall be, world without end. Amen.

Dear Reader,

I hope that reading this book has encouraged you to reflect on your own spiritual journey and helped to release the butterfly within. Should you wish to share your personal response, I will be pleased to receive your comments at the following address:

R.B.Fratianne,MD
PO Box #24358
Lyndhurst,Ohio 44124

Printed in the United States
124538LV00002B/13-18/A

9 781592 990184